GEOMETRIC INEQUALITIES

NEW MATHEMATICAL LIBRARY

published by

Random House and Yale University

for the

Monograph Project

of the

SCHOOL MATHEMATICS STUDY GROUP†

EDITORIAL PANEL

†The School Mathematics Study Group represents all parts of the mathematical
profession and all parts of the country. Its activities are aimed at the improvement
of teaching of mathematics in our schools. Further information can be obtained
from: School Mathematics Study Group, Drawer 2502 A, Yale Station,
New Haven, Connecticut.

GEOMETRIC

INEQUALITIES

by

Nicholas D. Kazarinoff

University of Michigan

4

RANDOM HOUSE

Illustrations by Florence W. Cochrane

First Printing

IN MEMORY OF
DONAT KONSTANTINOVICH

Note to the Reader

This book is one of a series written by professional mathematicians in order to make some important mathematical ideas interesting and understandable to a large audience of high school students and laymen. Most of the volumes in the *New Mathematical Library* cover topics not usually included in the high school curriculum; they vary in difficulty, and, even within a single book, some parts require a greater degree of concentration than others. Thus, while the reader needs little technical knowledge to understand most of these books, he will have to make an intellectual effort.

If the reader has so far encountered mathematics only in classroom work, he should keep in mind that a book on mathematics cannot be read quickly. Nor must he expect to understand all parts of the book on first reading. He should feel free to skip complicated parts and return to them later; often an argument will be clarified by a subsequent remark. On the other hand, sections containing thoroughly familiar material may be read very quickly.

The best way to learn mathematics is to *do* mathematics, and each book includes problems, some of which may require considerable thought. The reader is urged to acquire the habit of reading with paper and pencil in hand; in this way mathematics will become increasingly meaningful to him.

For the authors and editors this is a new venture. They wish to acknowledge the generous help given them by the many high school teachers and students who assisted in the preparation of these monographs. The editors are interested in reactions to the books in this series and hope that readers will write to: Editorial Committee of the NML series, in care of THE INSTITUTE OF MATHEMATICAL SCIENCES, NEW YORK UNIVERSITY, New York 3, N. Y.

The Editors

CONTENTS

Preface   3

Chapter 1.   **Arithmetic and Geometric Means**   7
    1.1   Fundamentals   7
    1.2   The Theorem of Arithmetic and Geometric Means   18

Chapter 2.   **Isoperimetric Theorems**   29
    2.1   Maxima and minima   29
    2.2   Isoperimetric theorems for triangles   32
    2.3   Isoperimetric theorems for polygons   44
    2.4   Steiner's attempt   58

Chapter 3.   **The Reflection Principle**   65
    3.1   Symmetry   65
    3.2   Dido's problem   67
    3.3   Steiner symmetrization   68
    3.4   Conic sections   71
    3.5   Triangles   75

Chapter 4.   **Hints and Solutions**   91

Index of Numbered Theorems   131

GEOMETRIC INEQUALITIES

Preface

When my father was alive, I often heard the words, "Niki, I have problem"; and more often than not the question which unfolded on our living-room blackboard dealt with an inequality. Nowadays, I like to think that it was partly because I never encountered questions at school which were even remotely similar to those with which I wrestled at home that I almost never found the solutions to any of the problems on the home blackboard. Mathematical curricula of today's secondary schools continue to ignore the topic of inequalities. Yet every mathematician knows that inequalities are important in all branches of mathematics, sometimes even more important than equalities.

In 1958 the Ann Arbor Public Schools gave me the opportunity to hold frequent mathematical discussions with an enthusiastic group of young people. These students, by their response and interest, stimulated me to write the present book. Their understanding and enjoyment of inequalities led me to believe that a careful exposition of some of the topics we discussed would be well received by a wider audience.

Geometric inequalities are especially appealing because their statements can be easily grasped; at the same time they provide an excellent introduction to creative mathematical thought and to the spirit of modern mathematics. The elementary inequalities that form the subject matter of this book have the further advantage of demanding and requiring only a clear head and a minimum of formal mathematical training in order to be understood: a year of high-school algebra and the fundamentals of plane geometry will usually be sufficient. On occasions I have used some trigonometry. Thus, some of the material can be profitably read by students in the second semester of plane geometry, while the book as a whole should be accessible to high-school juniors and seniors.

Another book in this series, *An Introduction to Inequalities*, by Edwin Beckenbach and Richard Bellman, provides additional background for the material I have presented. Moreover, Beckenbach's and Bellman's lively and leisurely study contains some analogous and some alternative treatments of many of the topics developed here.

Historically, geometric problems involving maxima and minima were studied before the invention of the calculus. The calculus is a powerful machine by which one can solve some of these problems without ingenuity. It is not a panacea, however, and anyone who intends to study or is now studying calculus, will find the material of Chapters 2 and 3 useful in understanding what the calculus can and cannot do.

Uninvited advice is usually ignored; yet I wish to offer some in the hope that it will be helpful. No book on mathematics can have enough illustrations and formulas. The thorough reader must always work with pencil and paper at hand. He will need them for constructing figures not provided in the text and for supplying missing steps between assertions or formulas. Often, drawing a portion of a figure in the text or rewriting a formula will clarify a troublesome point. The exercises and problems included in the text also play an important part. The reader who works on them as they appear will test and increase his understanding of what he reads, and he will be better prepared to proceed. The problems posed range from easy to difficult. I have even mentioned some unsolved problems. I have given solutions to selected problems in Chapter 4 in the hope that a reader who has worked on a problem will find it helpful to compare his solution with mine.

The manuscript was perused by Mrs. Jacqueline Lewis, Dr. Anneli Lax, and Professor Leo Zippin and was greatly improved by their criticisms, suggestions, and additions. I am particularly indebted to

Jacqueline Lewis and Anneli Lax for carefully checking the proofs and the solutions to the problems.

I am grateful to the Ann Arbor Board of Education for the opportunity to develop the contents of this book. I give hearty thanks to my student Robert Titiev of Ann Arbor High School who gave more than he received. Above all I acknowledge the inspiration and tutelage provided by my father, Donat K. Kazarinoff; his keenness of mind, his scholarship, and his magnificent spirit led me into the world of mathematics.

NICHOLAS D. KAZARINOFF
Moscow, U.S.S.R.
January, 1961

CHAPTER ONE

Arithmetic and Geometric Means

1.1 Fundamentals

Let us consider a straight line and choose a point O on it. Because
of our experience with rulers, yardsticks, and measuring tapes, we
can associate, in our mind's eye, a number with each point on the
line—a *positive* number if the point is to the right of O, a *negative*
number if the point is to the left of O, and *zero* if it is O. These numbers are called *real* numbers and may be written as decimals. The

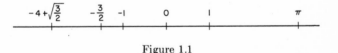

Figure 1.1

straight line we have associated with these numbers is called the *real
line*. In pictures we usually draw the real line horizontally and put
positive numbers to the right of zero. Some familiar real numbers are
1. $-3/2$, $-4 + \sqrt{5/3}$, and π. All the numbers we shall be work-
ing with are real numbers. At this point you have every right to
object and say that we really have not defined a real number. This is
correct. It is also true that a careful definition and discussion of real
numbers is at the foundation of mathematical analysis. Such a discussion is too sophisticated to be presented here but may be found,

7

for example, in *A Course of Pure Mathematics* by G. H. Hardy (Cambridge University Press, 1938). On the other hand, a thorough elementary treatment of some important properties of real numbers is given by Ivan Niven in *Numbers: Rational and Irrational*, another monograph in this series.

When we associate the real numbers with points on a straight line (as we have done in Fig. 1.1), we are implicitly asserting that the real-number system has certain properties. Since these properties are so fundamental and important, let me call attention to them. First of all, we take it for granted that in the set of all real numbers there is a subset which we call the set of positive real numbers, and that this set (call it P) has the following two properties:

I. If a is a real number, then exactly one of the following statements is true: a is in P, $-a$ is in P, a is zero.

II. If a and b are in P, then $a + b$ and $a \cdot b$ are in P.

Because the real-number system has this subset, we say it is *ordered*. We use this property of order when we associate the real numbers with the real line. If a is not in P and a is not zero, then we say a is negative. It can be *proved* that the real-number system is ordered. Moreover, it can be shown by means of the definition of multiplication of real numbers that if a and b are negative, then ab is positive, and that if a is positive and b is negative, then ab is negative. Of course, a product of two or more real numbers is zero if and only if at least one of the numbers is zero. If a is positive, we write $a > 0$.

The algebraic operations of addition and multiplication have geometric interpretations on the real line. Addition is often thought of as corresponding to a translation or shifting of the real line. Let us assume that the real line is horizontal as we look at it in our mind's

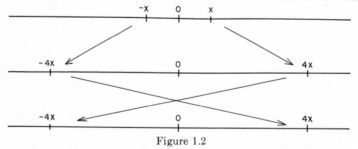

Figure 1.2

eye. Then in order to perform the operation of addition by 4, for example, we slide the real line to the right 4 units. To perform the operation of adding a real number b, we translate the real line to the right b units if b is positive or to the left $-b$ units if b is negative. Of course, if b is zero, then no translation is performed. Multiplication by a positive number is often thought of as being a stretching or contracting operation. In order to multiply by 4, for example, we stretch the real line, leaving the origin fixed, so that every point is exactly four times as far away from the origin as it originally was. To multiply by -4 we first perform a stretching by a factor of 4, and we then reflect each point of the stretched line with respect to 0. The order in which the operations of stretching and reflection are performed makes no difference. Multiplication by 1 leaves all points fixed; multiplication by zero compresses all points into a single point, the origin.

DEFINITION 1. $a > b$ (or equivalently $b < a$) if and only if $a - b > 0$, that is, if and only if there is a positive number h such that $a = b + h$.

"$a > b$" is read "a is greater than b";
"$a < b$" is read "a is less than b." The symbolic statement "$a < b$" is called an inequality. Geometrically we see that $a > b$ means that a is to the right of b on the real line. It follows from property (I) stated above that given any pair of real numbers a and b, exactly one of the statements $a > b$, $a = b$, and $a < b$ is true.

THEOREM 1. *The relation of inequality is transitive; that is, if $a > b$ and $b > c$, then $a > c$.*

PROOF. By the hypothesis of the theorem, there exist positive numbers h and k such that

$$a = b + h \quad \text{and} \quad b = c + k.$$

Hence,

$$a = (c + k) + h \quad \text{or} \quad a = c + (k + h).$$

But $k + h$ is positive since h and k are. By definition, this means that $a > c$. ∎†
If either one of the statements $a < b$ or $a = b$ holds, we write

---

† The symbol ∎ which appears at the end of the proof will appear at the end of many proofs as a signal meaning "this completes the proof."

$a \leq b$, which is read as "a is less than or equal to b." For example,

$$1 \leq 1 \quad \text{and} \quad 2 \leq 3,$$

since in each case one of the two possible alternatives "$<$" or "$=$" holds.

The next theorem tells how inequalities may be added.

THEOREM 2. *If $a > b$ and $c \geq d$, then $a + c > b + d$.*

The proof is just as easy as that of Theorem 1. You should construct the proof yourself.

Note that, if $a > b$ and $c > d$, ac might not be greater than bd. For example, $1 > -2$ and $2 > -3$, but $2 < 6$. The following theorem gives the rules of multiplication for inequalities involving positive numbers.

THEOREM 3. *If $a > b > 0$ and $c \geq d > 0$, then*

$$(1) \quad \ast ac > bd, \quad (2) \quad ac > bc, \quad \text{and} \quad (3) \quad \frac{1}{a} < \frac{1}{b}.$$

PROOF. By hypothesis there exist positive numbers h and k such that $a = b + h$ and $c = d + k$ unless $c = d$, in which case the equality $c = d + k$ still holds with $k = 0$. Hence,

$$ac = (b + h)(d + k) \quad \text{or} \quad ac = bd + bk + h(d + k).$$

The number $bk + h(d + k)$ is positive; therefore, by definition, $ac > bd$. You should complete the proof of the second conclusion by yourself. The third one follows from the second; for, choosing $c = 1/a$, we infer that

$$a \cdot \frac{1}{a} > b \cdot \frac{1}{a} \quad \text{or} \quad 1 > \frac{b}{a}.$$

Finally, by applying the second conclusion to the inequality $1 > b/a$, this time choosing $c = 1/b$, we find that

$$1 \cdot \frac{1}{b} > \frac{b}{a} \cdot \frac{1}{b} \quad \text{or} \quad \frac{1}{b} > \frac{1}{a}. \blacksquare$$

Before we state the next theorem, let us review the definition of a positive number raised to a fractional power. Let p be a positive rational number, and let a be a positive real number. (A number is rational if it can be written in the form m/n where m and n are integers, $n \neq 0$.) Since p is rational and positive, p may be written as m/n, where m and n are positive integers. The symbol a^m is defined to mean

$$\underbrace{a \cdot a \cdot \ \cdots \ \cdot a.}_{m \text{ factors}}$$

The symbol $a^{1/n}$ stands for that positive real number x such that $x^n = a$. Moreover,

$$a^{m/n} = (a^m)^{1/n}.$$

If q is a negative rational number, say $q = -p$ where p is positive, then

$$a^q = \frac{1}{a^p}.$$

Of course, $a^0 = 1$.

In this book we shall never have occasion to consider any number raised to an irrational power. However, for the sake of generality, we state the next theorem without restricting p to be rational. The problem of deciding whether such numbers as

$$(\sqrt{2})^{\sqrt{2}}, \qquad \pi^\pi$$

are rational or irrational once they have been defined is of great difficulty.

THEOREM 4. *If $a > b > 0$ and if $p > 0$, then $a^p > b^p$; if $p < 0$, then $a^p < b^p$.*

PROOF. We shall prove the theorem only in case p is a positive integer, and we shall leave to the reader the task of proving it for any rational number p. (A complete proof is given by E. Beckenbach and R. Bellman in their monograph *An Introduction to Inequalities*.) Let p be given. It follows from the hypothesis $a > b > 0$ and Theorem 3 that

$$a^2 > b^2.$$

If p is 2, we have nothing more to prove. Otherwise, we again apply

Theorem 3, this time to the inequalities

$$a > b > 0 \quad \text{and} \quad a^2 > b^2;$$

and we reach the conclusion

$$a^3 > b^3.$$

If p is 3, we are done. Otherwise, we continue in this way; and after exactly $p - 1$ such steps in all, we obtain the desired inequality

$$a^p > b^p. \ \blacksquare$$

The above theorems provide the basic facts about operations with inequalities which we shall need. Later on we often use them without calling attention to this fact by a specific reference. Before proceeding to use these theorems in our investigations, however, we shall apply them in some simple situations so as to see just how often we do use them and how important they therefore are. The solution to the following arithmetical problem illustrates them well.

PROBLEM. Which is larger, $\sqrt{7} + \sqrt{10}$ or $\sqrt{3} + \sqrt{17}$?

One way to decide is to find these numbers in a table of square roots or simply to compute the square roots to a few decimal places. We shall show that $\sqrt{3} + \sqrt{17} > \sqrt{7} + \sqrt{10}$. Our demonstration begins with a trivial observation and proceeds with the aid of the theorems to reach the desired conclusion. To see how the solution was discovered, one reverses the order of the reasoning. In doing the exercises which follow this example, you will find that the most natural method is to assume that the desired result is true and to deduce from it various other inequalities until you obtain one which you know is true. Next you must verify that each step can be reversed. If you succeed, you will have built a proof which leads from the known inequality to the one desired. The example above was deliberately chosen to have a long solution in order to illustrate the use of each of Theorems 1–4. Moreover, since the difference between $\sqrt{3} + \sqrt{17}$ and $\sqrt{7} + \sqrt{10}$ is small (about .05), it is not surprising that one cannot readily select the bigger of these two numbers.

SOLUTION. That $51 > 49$ is true by Definition 1 because $51 = 49 + 2$, and 2 is positive. Applying Theorem 4, with $p = 1/2$, to this inequality, we find $\sqrt{51} > 7$. From Theorem 3, with $a = \sqrt{51}$, $b = 7$, and $c = 12$, it follows that

$$12\sqrt{51} > 12 \cdot 7 = 84.$$

We find, by adding 213 to both sides of this inequation and using Theorem 2, that

$$213 + 12\sqrt{51} > 297.$$

But $297 > 280 = 4 \cdot 70$. Therefore by Theorem 1,

$$213 + 12\sqrt{51} > 4 \cdot 70.$$

We next observe that

$$213 = 9 + 204 = 9 + 4 \cdot 51 = 9 + \left(2\sqrt{51}\right)^2$$

and that

$$213 + 12\sqrt{51} = 9 + 2 \cdot 3 \cdot 2\sqrt{51} + \left(2\sqrt{51}\right)^2$$
$$= \left(3 + 2\sqrt{51}\right)^2.$$

Thus, by Theorem 4 with $p = 1/2$, we obtain the conclusion

$$3 + 2\sqrt{51} > 2\sqrt{70}.$$

This inequality can be rewritten in the form

$$3 + 17 + 2\sqrt{51} > 17 + 2\sqrt{70} \qquad \text{(Theorem 2)};$$

or, since $51 = 3 \cdot 17$ and $70 = 7 \cdot 10$, it can be rewritten in the form

$$\left(\sqrt{3}\right)^2 + 2 \cdot \sqrt{3} \cdot \sqrt{17} + \left(\sqrt{17}\right)^2$$
$$> \left(\sqrt{7}\right)^2 + 2 \cdot \sqrt{7} \cdot \sqrt{10} + \left(\sqrt{10}\right)^2,$$

which is the same as

$$\left(\sqrt{3} + \sqrt{17}\right)^2 > \left(\sqrt{7} + \sqrt{10}\right)^2.$$

Again applying Theorem 4 with $p = 1/2$, we obtain the promised result:

$$\sqrt{3} + \sqrt{17} > \sqrt{7} + \sqrt{10}. \blacksquare$$

As we have already remarked, there are much shorter ways of obtaining the same conclusion if one is willing to employ more advanced results of elementary algebra. The following exercises provide similar illustrations of our basic theorems.

Exercises

1. Show that $2 + \sqrt{7} < 5$.

2. Show that $2 + \sqrt[3]{7} < 4$.

3. Prove that if $a < 1$, then $2 - 2a > 0$.

4. Which is larger, $\sqrt{5/12} + \sqrt{1/5}$ or $\sqrt{1/3} + \sqrt{2/7}$? Prove your conjecture (guess).

5. Which is the greater number, $2(\sqrt{2} + \sqrt{6})$ or $3\sqrt{2 + \sqrt{3}}$? Prove your conjecture.

A slightly more sophisticated mode of using the fundamental theorems is given below. Let us consider the number

$$1 + \frac{1}{\sqrt{2}} + \frac{1}{\sqrt{3}} + \cdots + \frac{1}{\sqrt{9999}} + \frac{1}{100}.$$

How big is it? We might find it difficult to make an accurate guess. If we had a computing machine and enough time, we could make a computation of this number accurate to two decimal places or more. However, inequalities will help us to make a good estimate in a much shorter time. My purpose is just to familiarize you with the application of our basic theorems, so forgive me if I keep to textbook tradition and begin with "a rabbit out of a hat"; namely,

THEOREM 5. *For every positive integer* n,

$$2\sqrt{n + 1} - 2\sqrt{n} < \frac{1}{\sqrt{n}} < 2\sqrt{n} - 2\sqrt{n - 1}.$$

To prove this statement is not so difficult. The hard part is to think of it. You would not think of it unless you had already performed some experiments with inequalities. Experimentation is a typical occupation of mathematicians. We conduct many, many experiments, only our experiments are made with numbers, geometrical figures, and various other abstract objects. Our experiments, like those of natural scientists, are mostly failures. Occasionally they are successful, and we discover a theorem. Then it often happens that more work is needed to give a rigorous proof of the conjectured theorem, which we have come to believe is true by experiment. One might discover Theorem 5 by experimenting with the obvious statement that $\sqrt{n+1} > \sqrt{n}$. The following proof is just a successful experiment.

PROOF. Since $\sqrt{n+1} > \sqrt{n}$,

$$\frac{\sqrt{n+1} + \sqrt{n}}{2} > \frac{2\sqrt{n}}{2}. \qquad \text{(Why?)}$$

Therefore, by Theorem 3,

(1) $$\frac{2}{\sqrt{n+1} + \sqrt{n}} < \frac{1}{\sqrt{n}}.$$

Now $1/\sqrt{n}$ appears on the right. Since this is the quantity we are trying to estimate, it is natural next to eliminate the square roots in the denominator on the left. We recall the identity

$$(x + y)(x - y) = x^2 - y^2,$$

which we specialize to the form

$$(\sqrt{n+1} + \sqrt{n})(\sqrt{n+1} - \sqrt{n}) = (\sqrt{n+1})^2 - (\sqrt{n})^2.$$

The right-hand member of this identity is obviously the number 1. Hence, multiplying the numerator and denominator of the left-hand member of the last inequality by $\sqrt{n+1} - \sqrt{n}$, we find that

(2) $$\frac{2}{\sqrt{n+1} + \sqrt{n}} = 2(\sqrt{n+1} - \sqrt{n}).$$

The statements (1) and (2) together reveal that

$$2(\sqrt{n+1} - \sqrt{n}) < \frac{1}{\sqrt{n}},$$

which is one half of what we wish to prove. The observation that $\sqrt{n} > \sqrt{n-1}$ will enable you to prove the other half in a similar way. Try it! ▌ Which of our basic theorems have we used in this proof?

We shall now use Theorem 5 to solve the problem at hand. Let us "write down" the conclusion of the theorem in the ten thousand particular cases $n = 1, 2, \cdots, 9999, 10^4$. (In the case $n = 1$ we can afford to replace the right-hand estimate by an equality since the remaining 9999 cases will still involve inequalities. Doing this we get a better final estimate.):

$$2\sqrt{2} - 2 < \quad 1 \quad \leq 1,$$

$$2\sqrt{3} - 2\sqrt{2} < \frac{1}{\sqrt{2}} < 2\sqrt{2} - 2,$$

$$2\sqrt{4} - 2\sqrt{3} < \frac{1}{\sqrt{3}} < 2\sqrt{3} - 2\sqrt{2},$$

$$\cdot \quad \cdot \quad \cdot$$

$$2\sqrt{10^4} - 2\sqrt{9999} < \frac{1}{\sqrt{9999}} < 2\sqrt{9999} - 2\sqrt{9998}$$

and finally,

$$2\sqrt{10001} - 2\cdot 100 < \frac{1}{100} < 2\cdot 100 - 2\sqrt{9999}.$$

To obtain an approximation for the number we are considering, we add the corresponding members of these inequalities to each other one by one and observe that all but the first and last terms in the sum

$$2\sqrt{10001} - 2\cdot 100 + 2\cdot 100 - 2\sqrt{9999}$$

$$+ \cdots + 2\sqrt{3} - 2\sqrt{2} + 2\sqrt{2} - 2$$

of the left-hand members appear twice, once with a plus and once with a minus sign. The same is true of the sum of the right members. The inequalities we obtain after this addition are, by Theorem 2,

$$2\sqrt{10001} - 2 < 1 + \frac{1}{\sqrt{2}} + \cdots + \frac{1}{100} < 2\cdot 100 - 1.$$

Since $\sqrt{10001} > 100$, we have thus shown that

$$198 < 1 + \frac{1}{\sqrt{2}} + \cdots + \frac{1}{\sqrt{10^4}} < 199.$$

Of course, this estimate is a crude one, but it is much better than a mere guess.

If we adopt a suitable notation, we can write down the preceding argument more neatly. This notation is called *summation notation.* We define

$$\sum_{k=1}^{k=n} a_k \quad \text{to be} \quad a_1 + a_2 + \cdots + a_{n-1} + a_n \,.$$

We read "a_k" as "a sub k" or as "a k", and we read "$\sum_{k=1}^{k=n} a_k$" as "the sum from k equals 1 to k equals n of a sub k." We call k the *index of summation*. For example,

$$\sum_{k=1}^{k=4} k^2 = 1 + 4 + 9 + 16, \qquad \sum_{j=2}^{j=4} \log j = \log 2 + \log 3 + \log 4$$

and

$$\sum_{l=1}^{l=3} \frac{l!}{(3+l)!} = \frac{1!}{4!} + \frac{2!}{5!} + \frac{3!}{6!} = \frac{1}{24} + \frac{1}{60} + \frac{1}{120}.$$

(By definition, $k! = 1 \cdot 2 \cdot 3 \cdot \ \cdots \ \cdot k$ when k is a positive integer, and $0! = 1$. For example, $1! = 1$, $2! = 2$, $3! = 6$, $4! = 24$, $5! = 120$, and $6! = 720$.) If the choice of the index of summation is clear, as in these examples, we suppress it and simply write

$$\sum_1^4 k^2, \qquad \sum_2^4 \log j, \quad \text{and} \sum_1^3 \frac{l!}{(3+l)!}.$$

The number we estimated was $\sum_1^{10^4} 1/\sqrt{k}$. Theorem 5 states that $2(\sqrt{k+1} - \sqrt{k}) < 1/\sqrt{k} < 2(\sqrt{k} - \sqrt{k-1})$ for $k = 1, 2, \cdots$. Hence by Theorem 2 and from the fact that $2(\sqrt{2} - 1) < 1 \le 1$ (the last strict inequality is deducible from the inequality $8 < 9$ by means of our theorems), we conclude that

$$2(\sqrt{2} - 1) + \sum_2^{10^4} 2(\sqrt{k+1} - \sqrt{k}) < \sum_1^{10^4} \frac{1}{\sqrt{k}}$$
$$< 1 + \sum_2^{10^4} 2(\sqrt{k} - \sqrt{k-1})$$

or

$$2(\sqrt{10001} - 1) \le \sum_1^{10^4} \frac{1}{\sqrt{k}} < 2 \cdot 100 - 1.$$

From this result we obtained our final estimate. We shall continue to use summation notation whenever it is convenient.

PROBLEM 1. Show that for all positive integers n

$$\frac{1}{\sqrt{4n+1}} < \frac{1}{2} \cdot \frac{3}{4} \cdot \frac{5}{6} \cdot \ \cdots \ \cdot \frac{2n-1}{2n} \le \frac{1}{\sqrt{3n+1}}.$$

Can you improve this approximation?

1.2 The Theorem of Arithmetic and Geometric Means†

Consider the conjecture: Of all rectangles of area one, the square has the smallest perimeter. It is clear that a long, skinny rectangle of unit area has a much greater perimeter than a fat one having the same area, and the natural guess is that the square has the least perimeter as it is the fattest rectangle. We now have a credible conjecture, but how can we prove it? One possibility is to restate it in algebraic form and to attempt to prove the algebraic statement. Let us do this.

Suppose we are given a rectangle, and we choose our unit of measure so that its area is 1 sq. unit. If its length is x, then its width must be $1/x$ and its perimeter $2[x + (1/x)]$. The perimeter of the square with area 1 is 4. Thus we may restate our conjecture in the form

$$2\left(x + \frac{1}{x}\right) \geq 4 \quad \text{if} \quad x > 0,$$

with equality only if $x = 1$; or

$$(3) \qquad\qquad x + \frac{1}{x} \geq 2 \quad \text{if} \quad x > 0,$$

with equality only if $x = 1$. The next problem is to find a way of reducing this statement to one whose truth we already know. The thing to do is to multiply both sides of the inequality (3) by x. Then it becomes

$$x^2 + 1 \geq 2x \quad \text{if} \quad x > 0,$$

which is equivalent to

$$x^2 - 2x + 1 \geq 0 \quad \text{if} \quad x > 0.$$

The combination $(x - 1)^2$ appears to the eye now, and we rewrite the last inequality as

$$(x - 1)^2 \geq 0 \quad \text{if} \quad x > 0.$$

This statement is obvious since the square of a real number is never negative.

---

† Several proofs of this theorem, each different from the one given here, may be found in Chapter 4 of E. Beckenbach's and R. Bellman's *An Introduction to Inequalities* in this series.

If we can reverse our reasoning, we shall have discovered a proof of (3). Let us try to do so. By Theorem 2, the fact that

$$(x - 1)^2 \geq 0 \quad \text{(for any real number } x)$$

is equivalent to the inequality

$$x^2 + 1 \geq 2x.$$

If $x > 0$, we may apply Theorem 3 with $c = 1/x$ to this inequality and find that

$$x + \frac{1}{x} \geq 2 \quad \text{if} \quad x > 0.$$

Clearly, equality holds if and only if $x = 1$. ▮

Our main objective in this chapter is to generalize the simple theorem embodied in (3). The result (3) says that the sum of two positive numbers whose product is 1 is a minimum when they are equal. What can we say if more than two numbers are involved? A direct generalization of our inequality (3) is

THEOREM 6. *The sum of n positive numbers whose product is equal to 1 is always greater than or equal to n; equality holds if and only if all the numbers are equal (to 1). That is, if $a_i > 0$ ($i = 1, \cdots, n$) and if $a_1 \cdot a_2 \cdot \cdots \cdot a_{n-1} \cdot a_n = 1$, then*

$$\sum_{1}^{n} a_i \geq n,$$

with equality holding if and only if $a_i = 1$ for each i.

We postpone its proof to page 23.

A geometric interpretation of this theorem is: *If the volume of an n-dimensional box ("rectangular parallelepiped") is 1, the sum of the lengths of its edges is least when it is an n-dimensional cube.* You are most familiar with the cases $n = 2$ and $n = 3$ of this theorem. Of course, one cannot easily visualize a space with dimension greater than 3. Yet today mathematicians frequently consider problems in spaces of dimension greater than 3 and even in spaces of infinite dimension.

The case $n = 2$ of Theorem 6 may be stated in another form: If b_1 and b_2 are positive, then (use $a_1 = b_1/b_2$, $a_2 = b_2/b_1$)

$$(4) \qquad \frac{b_1}{b_2} + \frac{b_2}{b_1} \geq 2,$$

with equality only if $b_1 = b_2$.

PROBLEM 2. Given n positive numbers b_1, $\cdots$, b_n, what is the restatement of Theorem 6 in a form like that of inequality (4)?

DEFINITION 2. The *arithmetic mean* A of n numbers a_1, $\cdots$, a_n is

$$\frac{a_1 + a_2 + \cdots + a_n}{n}.$$

The arithmetic mean of a collection of numbers is often called their *average*.

If the truth of either one of two theorems implies the truth of the other, then we say that the two theorems are *equivalent*. The following proposition is equivalent to Theorem 6 but is more convenient to prove. We shall prove it first and then use it to prove Theorem 6.

THEOREM 7. *The product of n positive numbers with a given sum is greatest when they are all equal; that is, if $a_i > 0$ ($i = 1$, $\cdots$, n) and if $\sum_1^n a_i$ is fixed, say at nA, then*

$$(5) \qquad a_1 \cdot a_2 \cdot \ \cdots \ \cdot a_n \leq A^n,$$

with equality if and only if

$$a_1 = a_2 = \cdots = a_n.$$

Geometrically this theorem says: *Of all n-dimensional boxes which have the sum of the lengths of their edges the same, the n-dimensional cube has the greatest volume.* Still another equivalent geometric statement of the theorem is: *If a straight line segment is subdivided into a given finite number of parts, the product of their lengths is a maximum when they are equal.*

As we promised above, we shall first prove Theorem 7, and then we shall use this theorem to prove Theorem 6. The proof of Theorem 7 which is given below is based on the idea that if the n given numbers are not all equal (to their average), then, two by two, we can decrease those above the average and increase those below it until the numbers are all equal, all the while increasing their product. It would be difficult to work with n numbers all at once; it is much better to approach them two at a time. Since the proof is slightly complicated at first reading, an example which illustrates each step in the proof is presented in parallel with it.

PROOF OF THEOREM 7. If all the n numbers a_i originally given are equal to A, then equality holds in (5) as stated. If one of the given positive numbers is unequal to A, then there is at least one larger than A and at least one smaller than A.

Pick one smaller and one larger, call them a_1 and a_2, and write

$$a_1 = A - h \text{ and } a_2 = A + k.$$

Of course, h and k are positive.

We shall now change a_1 and a_2 so as to increase the product of the n numbers a_i while keeping their sum fixed at nA.
Let $a_1' = A$, and let
$$a_2' = A + k - h.$$

Then
$$a_1' + a_2' = 2A + k - h$$
$$= a_1 + a_2 ;$$

hence,
$$a_1' + a_2' + a_3 + \cdots + a_n$$
$$= \sum_1^n a_i = nA.$$

For example, suppose $n = 4$, and suppose the given positive numbers are 2, 3, 5, and 6. Then $A = 4$, and none of the given numbers is equal to A. We may choose $a_1 = 3$ and $a_2 = 6$. Then $a_1 = 4 - 1$ and $a_2 = 4 + 2$, so that $h = 1$ and $k = 2$.

We shall now change 3 and 6 so as to increase the product of the four given numbers while keeping their sum fixed at $16 = 4 \cdot A$.
Let $a_1' = 4$, and let
$$a_2' = 4 + 2 - 1 = 5.$$

Then
$$a_1' + a_2' = 4 + (4 + 2 - 1)$$
$$= (4 - 1) + (4 + 2)$$
$$= a_1 + a_2 ;$$

hence,

$$4 + 5 + 2 + 5$$
$$= 3 + 6 + 2 + 5 = 4 \cdot 4.$$

Clearly a_1' and a_2' are positive. We now have a second collection of n positive numbers whose sum is the same as the sum of the original n numbers.

We next observe that
$$a_1'a_2' > a_1a_2 .$$
Clearly, this is true since
$$a_1'a_2' = A(A + k - h)$$
$$= A^2 + (k - h)A,$$
and since
$$a_1a_2 = (A - h)(A + k)$$
$$-= A^2 + (k - h)A - hk,$$
from which it follows that
$$a_1'a_2' = a_1a_2 + h\cdot k,$$
where $h\cdot k$ is positive. By Definition 1, this means that
$$a_1'a_2' > a_1a_2 .$$
Thus,
$$a_1'\cdot a_2'\cdot a_3\cdot\ \cdots\ \cdot a_n$$
$$> a_1\cdot a_2\cdot a_3\cdot\ \cdots\ \cdot a_n .$$

We next observe that
$$4\cdot 5 > 3\cdot 6$$
since
$$4\cdot 5 = 4(4 + 2 - 1)$$
$$= 4^2 + (2 - 1)\cdot 4$$
and since
$$3\cdot 6 = (4 - 1)(4 + 2)$$
$$= 4^2 + (2 - 1)4 - 1\cdot 2.$$

Thus,
$$4\cdot 5\cdot 2\cdot 5 > 3\cdot 6\cdot 2\cdot 5.$$

If now $A = a_1' = a_2' = a_3 = \cdots = a_n$, there is nothing more to prove. If not, then there is at least one of the new set of n numbers a_1', a_2', a_3, $\cdots$, a_n which exceeds A and at least one which is less than A. Call them b_1 and b_2. Repeating the above argument with the roles of a_1 and a_2 taken by b_1 and b_2, we can find another set of n positive numbers with sum $n\cdot A$ whose product is larger than the product of the set a_1', a_2', a_3, $\cdots$, a_n.

If we repeat this process over and over again, then after at most $n - 1$ steps (including the first), we shall have constructed a set of n positive numbers all equal to A with their sum equal to nA and with their product larger than the product of any other n positive numbers with the same sum. (It requires thought to see that at most $n - 1$ steps are required.) ▌

In our example, the first set of numbers is $(3, 6, 2, 5)$. The second set is $(4, 5, 2, 5)$. After the second step, the set will be $(4, 4, 3, 5)$. $(b_1 = 2, b_2 = 5, b_1' = 4,$ and $b_2' = 3.)$ After the third and last step the set will be $(4, 4, 4, 4)$. Note that we could have chosen $a_1 = 2$ and $a_2 = 6$. Then the second set would have been $(4, 4, 3, 5)$ and the third set $(4, 4, 4, 4)$. Thus the argument may be completed in less than $n - 1$ steps for some sets of numbers.

We now use this theorem to prove Theorem 6.

PROOF OF THEOREM 6. We are given $a_i > 0$ $(i = 1, \cdots, n)$ with $a_1 \cdot a_2 \cdot \ \cdots \ \cdot a_n = 1$; we wish to prove that $\sum_1^n a_i \geq n$, with equality holding only if all the a_i equal 1. We reduce the problem to the previous one by a device which is used over and over again in mathematics. Namely, we divide each of the given numbers by the sum of all of them. When we do this, we obtain n new numbers whose sum is 1, and we can apply Theorem 7. Thus we let

$$ s = \sum_1^n a_i \quad \text{and} \quad b_i = \frac{a_i}{s} . $$

Since the arithmetic mean of the b_i's is

$$ \frac{1}{n} \sum_{i=1}^{i=n} b_i = \frac{1}{n} \sum_{i=1}^{i=n} \frac{a_i}{s} $$

$$ = \frac{1}{n} \cdot \frac{s}{s} = \frac{1}{n} , $$

we conclude from Theorem 7 that

$$ b_1 \cdot b_2 \cdot \ \cdots \ \cdot b_n \leq \left(\frac{1}{n}\right)^n , \text{ with equality only if } b_1 = \cdots = b_n = \frac{1}{n} . $$

In terms of the original numbers a_i , this statement is

$$ \frac{a_1 \cdot a_2 \cdot a_3 \cdot \ \cdots \ \cdot a_n}{s \cdot s \cdot s \cdot \ \cdots \ \cdot s} \leq \left(\frac{1}{n}\right)^n . $$

Equality holds only if $a_1 = a_2 = \cdots = a_n$. But by hypothesis $a_1 \cdot a_2 \cdot \ \cdots \ \cdot a_n = 1$. Therefore

$$ \frac{a_1 \cdot a_2 \cdot \ \cdots \ \cdot a_n}{s \cdot s \cdot \ \cdots \ \cdot s} = \left(\frac{1}{s}\right)^n \leq \left(\frac{1}{n}\right)^n $$

or, by Theorems 3 and 4,

$$ n \leq s, $$

with equality holding only if each $a_i = 1$. ∎

You yourself should demonstrate that Theorem 6 implies Theorem 7.

As a simple application of Theorem 6 for $n = 2$, we prove that *if*

x^2 is positive (that is, if x is a real number different from zero) then

$$\frac{x^2}{1 + x^4} \leq \frac{1}{2}.$$

Clearly if $x^2 > 0$,

$$\frac{x^2}{1 + x^4} = \frac{1}{\dfrac{1}{x^2} + x^2};$$

but by Theorem 6, $x^2 + (1/x^2) \geq 2$. Therefore, by Theorem 3,

$$\frac{x^2}{1 + x^4} \leq \frac{1}{2}$$

if x is not zero. Equality holds only if $x = \pm 1.$ ∎

Note. By setting $x = 0$ in the final inequality, we see that the inequality holds for $x = 0$ and thus for all x.

PROBLEM 3. Show that if $a > 1$, then $\log_{10} a + \log_a 10 \geq 2$.

DEFINITION 3. The *geometric mean* G of n positive numbers $a_1, \cdots, a_n$ is the nth root of their product:

$$G = \sqrt[n]{a_1 \cdot \cdots \cdot a_n}.$$

Theorems 6 and 7 are equivalent to the famous and useful *Theorem of Geometric and Arithmetic Means*:

THEOREM 8: *The geometric mean of n positive numbers is less than or equal to their arithmetic mean. The two means are equal if and only if the n numbers are equal.*

PROOF. The desired conclusion,

$$G \leq A,$$

follows directly from (5) if one applies Theorem 4 with $p = 1/n$. Equality holds only if each $a_i = G$. ∎

In a similar way, any one of the last three theorems can be used to prove each of the other two. You should attempt to do this.

We shall describe several geometrical applications of the last three theorems in the next chapter. For the present we content ourselves with two. The first is: *Of all three-dimensional boxes with a given surface area, the cube has the greatest volume.*

PROOF. Let a, b, and c denote the length, width, and height of a box with surface area S and volume V. Clearly,

$$V = abc \quad \text{and} \quad S = 2(ab + bc + ca).$$

The hypothesis that S is fixed means that the sum of the three quantities ab, bc, and ac is fixed. This suggests applying Theorem 7 or 8 to them. The result is

$$(ab \cdot bc \cdot ca)^{1/3} \leq \frac{ab + bc + ca}{3} \quad \text{or} \quad (V^2)^{1/3} \leq \frac{S}{6}.$$

Thus,

$$V \leq \left(\frac{S}{6}\right)^{3/2}.$$

Equality holds only if $ab = bc = ac$. From this result we see that the volume is greatest when $a = b = c$, that is, when the box is a cube. ∎

The second is: *The right circular cylinder of volume V which has the least surface area is the one whose diameter is equal to its altitude.*

PROOF. We denote the surface area, radius, and altitude of a right circular cylinder of volume V by S, r and h, respectively. Now,

$$S = 2\pi(r^2 + rh) \qquad \text{and} \qquad V = \pi r^2 h.$$

Therefore,

$$S = 2\pi\left(r^2 + \frac{V}{\pi r}\right)$$

$$= 2\pi\left(r^2 + \frac{V}{2\pi r} + \frac{V}{2\pi r}\right).$$

We can thus think of $S/(6\pi)$ as the arithmetic mean of the three numbers r^2, $V/(2\pi r)$ and $V/(2\pi r)$ so that, by Theorem 8,

$$\frac{S}{6\pi} \geq \left(\frac{V^2}{4\pi^2}\right)^{1/3}.$$

But the right-hand member of this inequality is fixed. Therefore, S is smallest when equality holds, that is, when

$$r^2 = \frac{V}{2\pi r} \qquad \text{or} \qquad V = 2\pi r^3.$$

Thus, S is smallest when $2r = h$. ∎

PROBLEM 4. Prove that if a and b are positive,

$$(6) \qquad \sqrt[n+1]{ab^n} \leq \frac{a + nb}{n + 1} \qquad (n = 1, 2, 3, \cdots)$$

with equality holding only if $a = b$.

PROBLEM 5. Show that for $n \geq 2$,

$$n! < \left(\frac{n + 1}{2}\right)^n.$$

PROBLEM 6. Prove that if a, b, and c are not negative, then

$$9abc \leq (a + b + c)(bc + ca + ab).$$

PROBLEM 7. Use the inequality (3) of this section to show that if $a_i > 0 \quad (i = 1, 2, \cdots, n)$, then

$$\left(\sum_1^n a_i\right)\left(\sum_1^n \frac{1}{a_i}\right) \geq n^2.$$

In what follows we shall occasionally employ the notion of absolute value. We next give its definition and briefly discuss its use.

DEFINITION 4. The *absolute value* of a number x is x if $x \geq 0$ and is $-x$ if $x < 0$.

The absolute value of x is denoted $|x|$. Definition 4 says that

$$|x| = x \quad \text{if} \quad x \geq 0$$

and

$$|x| = -x \quad \text{if} \quad x < 0.$$

It follows from this definition that $|x|^2 = x^2$ and, more importantly, that

$$|x| = \sqrt{x^2}.$$

For example,

$$|-6| = \sqrt{(-6)^2} = \sqrt{36} = 6.$$

If the points on a straight line are labeled with real numbers as explained on p. 7, then $|x|$ is just the distance from the point x, or $-x$, to the origin. The number $|x - y|$ is the distance from the point x on the real line to the point y on the real line. It is also the distance from the point $-x$ to the point $-y$. Clearly,

$$| x - y | = | y - x |.$$

If there were someone who did not have an intuitive grasp of the concept of the distance between points on a straight line, then the preceding remarks could be used to *define* the concept for him. As a matter of convenience, in subsequent chapters we shall frequently use the symbols $\overline{AB}$ to denote the distance between geometric points A and B.

It is important to note that a single inequality such as

$$| x | < | y |$$

is equivalent to two simultaneous inequalities. For example, $-3 < x < 3$ is equivalent to $| x | < 3$. The equation $| x | = 3$ has two roots: 3 and -3. Obviously, $| x | = 0$ if and only if $x = 0$.

PROBLEM 8. Show that $| a | - | b | \leq | a + b | \leq | a | + | b |$. What is the geometric interpretation of these inequalities?

CHAPTER TWO

Isoperimetric Theorems

2.1 Maxima and minima

The problem, which we met in Section 1.2, of determining the rectangle of smallest perimeter among all those with area 1 is but one of the problems of maxima and minima in geometry. Problems of this kind were studied by Greek geometers before the birth of Christ. Of course, it is uncertain who were the first people to pose problems involving maxima and minima, but many arise quite naturally and might have, and might yet occur to people in a primitive culture. For example, what is there about the shape of a circular cylinder that causes many flower stems, tree trunks, and many other natural objects to take its shape, why are small water droplets and bubbles that float in air approximately spherical, and why does a herd of reindeer form a circle if attacked by wolves? Admittedly, these problems involve mathematics only indirectly, but they are capable of stimulating mathematical thought. There are problems which are more directly mathematical. For example, what shape should a plot of ground be so that a given length of fence will enclose the greatest area, and what are the dimensions of a cylindrical container so that it will contain the greatest volume for a given surface area? Can you think of other examples? The Greeks were mostly interested in natural phenomena such as the hexagonal arrangement of cells in honeycomb, but they also had practical problems. Many were connected with war (just as in our own day!) such as the problem of estimating the size of an enemy's camp. One would not like to be in the enemy's neighborhood at dawn with too few men. The assumption was that the number of men was roughly proportional to the area covered by their camp. It was common to measure the size of an enemy's camp by the length of its perimeter. Often this procedure gave misleading conclusions, and hence, a better, more mathematical solution to the problem was sought.

The mathematical questions underlying many of the examples cited above are of two kinds: Of all geometric figures having a certain property, which has the greatest area or volume; and of all figures having a certain property, which has the least perimeter or surface area? Loosely speaking, both these problems are called isoperimetric problems; "isoperimetric" means "with the same perimeter." The famous Isoperimetric Theorem, which took mankind over two thousand years to prove after it was discovered, gives the solution to a broad class of these questions.

THEOREM 9 (The Isoperimetric Theorem).
(A) *Of all plane figures with a given perimeter, the circle has the greatest area.*
(B) *Of all plane figures with a given area, the circle has the least perimeter.*

In language appropriate to three-dimensional space, this theorem becomes:
(A) *Of all solids with a given surface area, the sphere has the greatest volume.*
(B) *Of all solids with a given volume, the sphere has the least surface area.*

In this chapter we shall discuss several isoperimetric theorems. We begin with some simple ones, and we shall conclude with a discussion of the Isoperimetric Theorem itself. First permit me to mention a little of the history of this illustrious theorem. The solution of the isoperimetric problem for rectangles was already known to Euclid, who lived about 300 B.C.; and it was probably known long before, as many of the theorems in Euclid's *Elements* are not Euclid's original work. Archimedes (287–212 B.C.), one of the greatest mathematicians of all time, knew the statement of the Isoperimetric Theorem. By the beginning of the Christian era, the study of maxima and minima in geometry had considerably advanced. We know, in fact, that Zenodoros, who lived sometime between 200 B.C. and 90 A.D., wrote a book entitled *Isoperimetric Figures*. There are, unfortunately, no copies of his book left for us to read; but his results were described and proved again by Pappus of Alexandria, who lived about 300 A.D. We do have copies of his work [Pappus d'Alexandrie, *La Collection Mathématique*, Book V, edited by P. VerEcke, Brouwer, Paris (1933)]. Pappus, of course, knew the Isoperimetric Theorem and, what is more interesting, thought he had a proof of the theorem that a circle has a greater area than any polygon with the same perimeter. In the main, his work is exact and easy to follow.

Little progress was made from the work of the Greek geometers until that of Simon Lhuilier, a Swiss of the late eighteenth century, and of his fellow countryman Jacob Steiner (1796–1863) after him. The methods developed by Lhuilier and Steiner in their research have had great influence on mathematics and are still being used. The methods of Steiner were essentially geometric (rather than algebraic or analytic), that is, synthetic methods. In other words, he reasoned from the geometrical properties of figures without resorting to theorems of algebra and calculus and the method of analytic geometry. (You used, or are using, synthetic methods in your study of plane geometry.) Through his methods Steiner solved many problems which had resisted solution even with the help of the calculus "invented" by Newton and Leibniz in the seventeenth century. In turn, Steiner's work stimulated a growth in analytical mathematics, especially the calculus of variations. This was because of the error in his proofs of the Isoperimetric Theorem. The error was found by the German mathematician Karl Weierstrass, the founder of the rigor characteristic of modern mathematics. In order to fill the gap in Steiner's proofs, Weierstrass had to develop the calculus further. He had to put the whole subject upon a rigorous, logically sound basis. Steiner's work possesses a great deal of charm. I have tried to conduct the discussion of this chapter in the spirit of Steiner and to illustrate his methods at every opportunity.

2.2 Isoperimetric theorems for triangles

Polygons are among the simplest geometric figures, and triangles are the most elementary figures among polygons. For this reason the foundation of our investigations of isoperimetric theorems consists of two statements about triangles.

THEOREM 10.

(A) *Of all triangles with a common base and perimeter, the isosceles triangle has the greatest area.*

(B) *Of all triangles with a common base and area, the isosceles triangle has the smallest perimeter.*

We shall also make use of a theorem which can be proved in the same way as Theorem 10A is proved, and which in fact is a stronger theorem.

THEOREM 10A′. *If two triangles have the same base and the same perimeter, the one with the smaller difference in the lengths of its legs has the larger area.*

We are now going to prove Theorem 10A; and in order to give the broadest possible understanding of the theorem, we shall prove it in two quite different ways and indicate still another. It is not common in textbooks to give several proofs of a theorem, but I feel it should be. Not only does this procedure lead to a deeper understanding of results by revealing their connections with various ideas, but it takes into account the fact that the proof which is most easily understood by you might be difficult for a friend to grasp, while he or she might best understand another proof.

I strongly urge you in reading the proofs that follow to construct your own figure or figures in step with the proofs. A partially constructed figure is often more revealing than the finished illustrations appearing in a text. You should experiment with variations of your own as they occur to you. Find out what does not work as well as what does. This is a way one discovers a proof of a theorem or understands a proof presented on a silver blackboard.

PROOF 1 OF THEOREM 10A. Let ABC be an isosceles triangle with base AB, and let ABD be another triangle with the same base and perimeter. This implies that $\overline{AC} + \overline{BC} = \overline{AD} + \overline{BD}$. (The symbol $\overline{XY}$ denotes the distance from X to Y.) Since ABD has the same perimeter as ABC but is not isosceles, it must have one side, say AD,

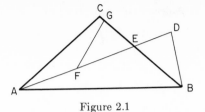

Figure 2.1

such that $\overline{AD} > \overline{AC}$ and another side BD such that $\overline{BD} < \overline{AC}$ (see Fig. 2.1). It also must be that AD intersects BC at E, where $E \neq D$. If it did not, either D would be interior to, or on the boundary of, $\triangle ABC$ [see Fig. 2.2(a)] or C would be interior to, or on the boundary of, $\triangle ABD$ [see Fig. 2.2(b)]. That neither of these situations can occur follows from the theorem which states that the sum of the lengths of two sides of a triangle is greater than the length of the third side. The reasoning is simple but perhaps not obvious, and therefore I describe it.

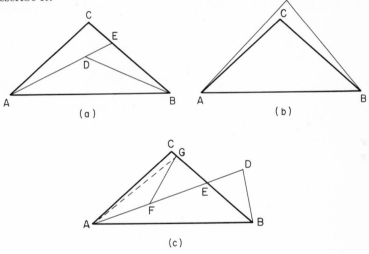

Figure 2.2

First we suppose D is interior to $\triangle ABC$ and that E is the intersection of BC and AD extended. Then the theorem just quoted provides the inequalities

$$\overline{AC} + \overline{CE} > \overline{AD} + \overline{DE}$$

and

$$\overline{DE} + \overline{EB} > \overline{BD}.$$

Therefore, by Theorem 2,

$$\overline{AC} + (\overline{CE} + \overline{EB}) + \overline{DE} > \overline{AD} + \overline{BD} + \overline{DE}$$

or

$$\overline{AC} + \overline{CB} > \overline{AD} + \overline{BD}.$$

This last statement contradicts the hypothesis that

$$\overline{AC} + \overline{BC} = \overline{AD} + \overline{BD}.$$

If $D = E$, then the above reasoning again leads us to a contradiction of the hypothesis. Thus D is exterior to $\triangle ABC$ as we claimed.

Next, suppose that C is inside or on the boundary of $\triangle ABD$ as pictured in Fig. 2.2(b). If this were so, then by the same reasoning as before, we could deduce that $\overline{AD} + \overline{DB} > \overline{AC} + \overline{CB}$, which again contradicts the hypothesis. We now proceed with the proof of the theorem.

Let F be on AE with $\overline{EF} = \overline{EB}$. This choice of F is possible since $\overline{BE} < \overline{AE}$, a fact guaranteed by the inequality

Angle EAB < Angle CAB = Angle EBA.

Also construct EG on EC (perhaps extended) with $\overline{EG} = \overline{ED}$. We shall prove that G actually does lie between C and E. Since $\triangle EFG$ is congruent to $\triangle EBD$, we will then know that the area of $\triangle ABC$ is greater than the area of $\triangle ABD$. To prove that G lies between C and E, we first observe that

$$\overline{FG} = \overline{BD} \qquad (\triangle EFG \cong \triangle EBD)$$

and

$$\overline{AC} + \overline{BC} = \overline{AD} + \overline{BD} \qquad \text{(by hypothesis)}.$$

We now see that

$$\overline{AC} + \overline{BC} = \overline{AF} + \overline{FD} + \overline{FG}$$
$$= \overline{AF} + \overline{BG} + \overline{FG}$$
$$= \overline{AF} + \overline{BC} \pm \overline{CG} + \overline{FG}$$

or

$$\overline{AC} = \overline{AF} \pm \overline{CG} + \overline{FG},$$

the minus sign or the plus sign being used according as G lies between

E and C or beyond C. The alternative

$$\overline{AC} = \overline{AF} + \overline{CG} + \overline{FG}$$

is impossible since a straight-line distance is the shortest distance between two points; hence, G lies between E and C.

Let the area of a triangle XYZ be denoted by $T(XYZ)$. Then

$$
\begin{aligned}
T(ABC) &= T(ABE) + T(EFG) & + [T(AFG) + T(ACG)] \\
&= [T(ABE) + T(BDE)] + [T(AFG) + T(ACG)] \\
&= T(ABD) & + [T(AFG) + T(ACG)].
\end{aligned}
$$

Consequently,

$$T(ABC) > T(ABD). \ \blacksquare$$

Before we go on to the second proof of Theorem 10A, let us agree upon some notation and recall a theorem from plane geometry. Once and for all let us agree that if ABC is a triangle, then a, b, and c denote the lengths of its sides; namely,

$$a = \overline{BC}, \qquad b = \overline{AC}, \qquad c = \overline{AB}.$$

Also let us agree that P is its perimeter, and T is its area.

The theorem we wish to recall is due to Heron.

THEOREM (Heron). *For any triangle ABC,*

$$(7) \qquad 16T^2 = [(a + b)^2 - c^2][c^2 - (a - b)^2],$$

and

$$(7') \qquad 16T^2 = P(P - 2a)(P - 2b)(P - 2c).$$

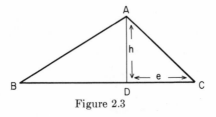

Figure 2.3

PROOF. Let h denote the length of the altitude AD (see Fig. 2.3), and let $e = \overline{DC}$. Then

$$c^2 - (a - e)^2 = h^2 = b^2 - e^2.$$

Thus,

$$c^2 - a^2 + 2ae = b^2;$$

or, since $a \neq 0$,

$$e = \frac{1}{2a} [a^2 + b^2 - c^2].$$

The area of a triangle is half the product of the lengths of the base and the altitude. Using this theorem and the value $b^2 - e^2$ for h^2, we find that

$$2T = ah,$$

$$4T^2 = a^2h^2 = a^2(b^2 - e^2) = a^2[b^2 - \frac{1}{4a^2}(a^2 + b^2 - c^2)^2],$$

$$16T^2 = 4a^2b^2 - (a^2 + b^2 - c^2)^2,$$

$$= [2ab + (a^2 + b^2 - c^2)][2ab - (a^2 + b^2 - c^2)],$$

$$= [(a + b)^2 - c^2][c^2 - (a - b)^2].$$

This proves formula (7). Since each factor of the right member is a difference of two squares, it can be further factored and written in the form

$$(a + b + c)(a + b - c)(c + a - b)(c - a + b).$$

If we now write P in place of $a + c + b$, we observe that we can write (7) as (7′). ∎

You are perhaps more familiar with the theorem in the less convenient form

$$T = [s(s - a)(s - b)(s - c)]^{1/2},$$

where $s = P/2$. This is obtained by dividing both sides of (7′) by 4 and by then taking square roots of both members of the resulting equality. The second proof of Theorem 10A is based upon (7).

PROOF 2 OF THEOREM 10A. Examining (7), we notice that $16T^2$ is a product of two factors. If P and c are fixed, then so is $(a + b)$; thus the first factor is fixed. Hence the product $16T^2$ increases if the second factor increases. This is the case if $a - b$ decreases. The second factor is greatest when $a - b = 0$; hence T is greatest when $a = b$. ∎

EXERCISE. Use the reasoning employed in one of the two proofs of Theorem 10A to prove Theorem 10A'.

PROBLEM 9. Give a third proof of Theorem 10A using Theorem 10B. *Hint.* Read the proof that Theorem 10A implies Theorem 10B, below.

Heron's formula can also be used to prove Theorem 10B.

PROOF OF THEOREM 10B. Since c is fixed by hypothesis, P is smallest when $a + b$ is least. But since T is also fixed by hypothesis, the product $16T^2$ of the two factors $[(a + b)^2 - c^2]$ and $[c^2 - (a - b)^2]$ in (7) is constant. Hence, the first factor is smallest when the second is greatest. But the first factor in Heron's formula (7) is least when $a + b$ is least. Thus, $a + b$ is least when the second factor is greatest, that is, when $a - b = 0$, or $a = b$. ■

Another proof of Theorem 10B, which is independent of the one above, is contained in the demonstration found at the end of Section 3.1, in Chapter 3.

Theorems 10A and B are equivalent, as we can easily show. We shall give a full demonstration of the fact that the first implies the second. The converse is posed as Problem 9.

PROOF THAT THEOREM 10A IMPLIES THEOREM 10B. Let $\triangle$ † be any triangle with area T and perimeter P. Suppose $\triangle_1$ is an isosceles triangle with the same base and area as $\triangle$ but with perimeter P_1. We shall prove that $P \geq P_1$, with equality only if $\triangle$ is isosceles.

Suppose $\triangle_2$ is an isosceles triangle with the same base as $\triangle$, with perimeter P and with area T_2. Theorem 10A guarantees that

$$T_2 > T.$$

Since $\triangle_1$ and $\triangle_2$ have the same base and are both isosceles, this implies that the perimeter P of $\triangle_2$ (and hence of $\triangle$) is larger than P_1. ■

It is easy to illustrate the above proof with an example. Let $\triangle$ be a right-angled triangle with sides 3, 4, and 5 units in length. Then $T = 6$ and $P = 12$. See Fig. 2.4.

Let BC be the base of $\triangle$. Then $\triangle_1$, an isosceles triangle with the same base and area as $\triangle$, has legs of length $\sqrt{13}$ and perimeter

† It is occasionally advantageous to use the symbol "△" (read "delta") as the name of a particular triangle instead of as a symbol for the word "triangle." This is the case in the present instance.

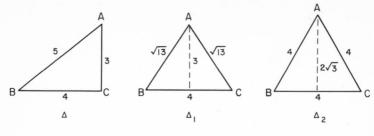

Figure 2.4

$P_1 = 4 + 2\sqrt{13}$. Clearly, $\sqrt{13} < 4$; hence

$$P_1 = 4 + 2\sqrt{13} < 4 + 2 \cdot 4 = 12 = P.$$

Now $\triangle_2$, an isosceles triangle with the same base and perimeter as $\triangle$, has legs of length 4 (in fact, $\triangle_2$ is equilateral), and $T_2 = 4\sqrt{3}$. As expected, $T_2 > T$, since $4\sqrt{3} > 6$.

A natural and good question which could now be asked is: are there theorems related to Theorem 10 which we can state and prove? Before you proceed with your reading, try to imagine some. The most obvious one from the point of view of its connection with Theorem 10 is the isoperimetric theorem for triangles; namely,

THEOREM 11A. *Of all triangles with a given perimeter, the equilateral triangle has the greatest area.*

We shall present three proofs of this theorem, each with its own merits. The first proof is essentially an illustration of Theorem 7, see page 20, and thus really depends upon the Theorem of Arithmetic and Geometric Means. The second one is long but illustrates a method of great importance in mathematics. The third is almost as short as the first and reflects geometrically the algebraic construction in the proof of Theorem 7.

PROOF 1. Let ABC be any triangle. Since P is fixed, formula (7) tells us that $16T^2$ is greatest when $(P - 2a)(P - 2b)(P - 2c)$ is greatest. According to Theorem 7, this maximum is achieved when $P - 2a = P - 2b = P - 2c$, that is, when $a = b = c$. Consequently, T is a maximum for an equilateral triangle. ∎

PROOF 2. This proof is due to Simon Lhuilier. It involves the method of successive approximations. Since this method is in constant use among mathematicians even today, it is well worth presenting to you in this simple context. It will also give you the opportunity to become better acquainted with the notion of a limit.

Suppose that $\triangle_1$ is any triangle and that it has perimeter P and area T_1. So that we shall have something to discuss, let us also agree that $\triangle_1$ is not equilateral. We shall show that if $\triangle$ is the equilateral triangle with area T and perimeter P, then $T > T_1$. We shall do this by constructing an infinite sequence of triangles

$$\triangle_1, \triangle_2, \cdots, \triangle_n, \cdots,$$

each with perimeter P and such that each one after the first has a greater area than its predecessor. As n becomes larger and larger, the triangles $\triangle_n$ will become more and more like the equilateral triangle $\triangle$, and their areas will approach the area of $\triangle$. We shall make this more precise a little later.

We now define the sequence $\{\triangle_n\}$. The first triangle in the sequence is $\triangle_1$. Suppose that its base is of length b and its legs are of length a_1 and a_2. Let $s_1 = a_1 + a_2$. The second triangle in the sequence is the isosceles triangle $\triangle_2$ with base b and each leg $\frac{1}{2}s_1$ in length. Let $s_2 = b + \frac{1}{2}s_1$. The third triangle in the sequence is the isosceles triangle $\triangle_3$ with base $\frac{1}{2}s_1$ and each leg $\frac{1}{2}s_2$ in length. For $n \geq 3$, having constructed the isosceles triangle $\triangle_n$, we choose $s_n = \frac{1}{2}(s_{n-2} + s_{n-1})$; and we construct the isosceles triangle $\triangle_{n+1}$ with base $\frac{1}{2}s_{n-1}$ and each leg $\frac{1}{2}s_n$ in length. We continue this process indefinitely. Each triangle in the sequence constructed has perimeter P because in each step of our construction, one side of the new triangle has the same length as one side of its predecessor, and the sum of the lengths of the other two sides is kept fixed.

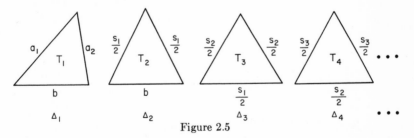

Figure 2.5

We know that a solution to our problem exists since we have already given one proof of the theorem. The question we must now face is: Is it true that in some reasonable sense the equilateral triangle with perimeter P is the limit of the sequence $\{\triangle_n\}$? We shall attempt to support strongly an affirmative answer. The reader must not lightly dismiss the possibility that the sequence $\{\triangle_n\}$ might have no limit. We shall discuss this sort of eventuality in Section 2.4 after we have considered more examples.

The areas and perimeters of the triangles $\triangle_n$ are to be considered. Let T_n be the area of $\triangle_n$. Since $\triangle_n$ and $\triangle_{n+1}$ each have a side of length $\frac{1}{2}s_{n-1}$ and have the same perimeter, it follows from Theorem 10A that $T_{n+1} > T_n$ for each n.

Also, our triangles become more and more nearly equilateral. To see this observe that, for each n, the triangle $\triangle_n$ has two sides of length $\frac{1}{2}s_{n-1}$ and that the third side has length $\frac{1}{2}s_{n-2}$. We may use the difference

$$\tfrac{1}{2}(s_{n-1} - s_{n-2})$$

between the lengths of a pair of unequal sides to measure how much the nth triangle deviates from being an equilateral triangle. We shall see from the following calculations that these differences become smaller as n increases and, in fact, approach zero.

$$
\begin{aligned}
s_2 - s_1 &= (b + \tfrac{1}{2}s_1) & - s_1 &= b - \tfrac{1}{2}s_1, \\
s_3 - s_2 &= (\tfrac{1}{2}s_1 + \tfrac{1}{2}s_2) & - s_2 &= \tfrac{1}{2}(s_1 - s_2) = -\tfrac{1}{2}(b - \tfrac{1}{2}s_1), \\
s_4 - s_3 &= (\tfrac{1}{2}s_2 + \tfrac{1}{2}s_3) & - s_3 &= \tfrac{1}{2}(s_2 - s_3) = 2^{-2}(b - \tfrac{1}{2}s_1), \\
&\;\;\vdots & &\;\;\vdots \\
s_n - s_{n-1} &= (\tfrac{1}{2}s_{n-2} + \tfrac{1}{2}s_{n-1}) - s_{n-1} &= (-1)^{n-2}2^{-(n-2)}(b - \tfrac{1}{2}s_1), \\
s_{n+1} - s_n &= (\tfrac{1}{2}s_{n-1} + \tfrac{1}{2}s_n) & - s_n &= (-1)^{n-1}2^{-(n-1)}(b - \tfrac{1}{2}s_1), \\
&\;\;\vdots & &\;\;\vdots
\end{aligned}
$$

I now ask you to be indulgent and to allow me to appeal to your common sense and intuition for the remainder of the proof. The above estimates of the differences $s_{n+1} - s_n$ guarantee that

$$\lim_{n \to \infty} (s_{n+1} - s_n) = 0.$$

This statement is read as "the limit, as n becomes infinite, of the difference $(s_{n+1} - s_n)$ is zero". We define this statement to mean precisely this: Given a positive number e (any one, large or small), there can be found a positive integer N such that

$$(8) \qquad\qquad | s_{n+1} - s_n | < e$$

for all integers n greater than N. The important thing to notice is that one fixes e once and for all, and then one looks for N. One can establish (8) by noticing that

$$\mid s_{n+1} - s_n \mid = \frac{\mid b - \frac{1}{2}s_1 \mid}{2^{n-1}}$$

and that, since $\mid b - \frac{1}{2}s_1 \mid$ is fixed, the right member becomes as small as one desires if n is chosen large enough. Since each triangle $\triangle_n$ has perimeter P, it can be shown, using (8), that

$$(9) \qquad \lim_{n \to \infty} s_n = \frac{2P}{3} \quad \text{and} \quad \lim_{n \to \infty} T_n = T \,.$$

(By definition, the statement $\lim_{n \to \infty} T_n = T$ means that given any positive number e, there can be found a positive integer N such that $\mid T_n - T \mid \, < \, e$ for all integers n greater than N.) The conclusion embodied in (9) can be rigorously proved using (8). However, such a proof belongs to the theory of limits and is outside the scope of our study. Finally, it is clear that since $T_{n+1} > T_n$, $T > T_n$ for any n. In particular, $T > T_1$. ∎

The third proof of Theorem 11A is due to Jacob Steiner. By a clever geometric construction Steiner neatly avoided using the method of successive approximations employed by Lhuilier.

PROOF 3. Consider any triangle $\triangle_1$ with perimeter P, area T_1 and sides of lengths a, b, and c, where $a \geq b \geq c$ so that $P/3 \geq c$. We suppose for the sake of argument that c is closer to $P/3$ than a is, and we let

$$h = \frac{P}{3} - c > 0 \,.$$

Instead of constructing an isosceles triangle $\triangle_2$ as we did in the last proof, we now construct a triangle $\triangle_2$ (see Fig. 2.6) with base b and legs of lengths $P/3$ and $a - h$ and call its area T_2. (You should carry out this construction youself with ruler and compass.) Since

$$(a - h) + \frac{P}{3} = a + \left(\frac{P}{3} - h \right) = a + c \,,$$

$\triangle_2$ has perimeter P. We next note that the difference between the lengths a and c of the legs of $\triangle_1$ is greater than the difference between the lengths of the legs of $\triangle_2$; that is,

$$a - c > (a - h) - \frac{P}{3} \,.$$

This is true because from the inequality

$$c = \frac{P}{3} - h < \frac{P}{3} + h \,,$$

it follows that

$$a - c > a - \left(\frac{P}{3} + h\right) = (a - h) - \frac{P}{3} \,.$$

We now apply Theorem 10A′ (see page 32) to the triangles $\triangle_1$ and $\triangle_2$ and conclude that

$$T_2 > T_1 \,.$$

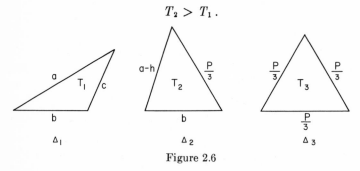

Figure 2.6

We next construct an isosceles triangle $\triangle$ with base $P/3$ and legs of length

$$\frac{1}{2}\left[\frac{P}{3} + h + c\right].$$

Since this number is $P/3$, the triangle $\triangle$ is equilateral; and by Theorem 10A, its area T is greater than T_2. Thus $T > T_1$. A similar argument can be carried out if

$$a - \frac{P}{3} < \frac{P}{3} - c. \qquad \blacksquare$$

The companion theorem to Theorem 11A is

THEOREM 11B. *Of all triangles with a given area, the equilateral triangle has the least perimeter.*

PROBLEM 10. Show that Theorems 11A and B are equivalent.

PROBLEM 11. Use Heron's formula (7) to prove Theorem 11B.

PROBLEM 12. Of all triangles circumscribed about a given circle,

which has the least area? Which has the smallest perimeter? Prove
your conjectures.

Hint. Use the method by which the equivalence of Theorems 10A
and B is demonstrated.

PROBLEM 13. Of all triangles inscribed in a given circle, which has
the largest area? Which has the largest perimeter? Prove your conjectures.

Remark. It is quite difficult to give a rigorous elementary proof although the result is reasonably obvious.

PROBLEM 14. Of all triangles with a given perimeter (or area), which
has the smallest circumscribing circle? Prove your claims.

Hint. Use the result of Problem 13.

It is time to call to attention a fact which you may have already
noticed: isoperimetric theorems come in pairs. Theorems 9, 10, and
11 are examples of this phenomenon. The situation is this. Suppose
that C is a class of plane figures for which the following isoperimetric
theorem holds:

(*) *Of all figures with perimeter P in the class C, the "blank" has the
greatest area.*

Suppose further that all "blanks" are similar. Then the following
statement is also a theorem:

(**) *Of all figures with area A in class C, the "blank" has the least
perimeter.*

As an example, let C be the class of all triangles, and let the "blanks"
be the equilateral triangles. Then (*) gives us Theorem 11A and (**)
gives us Theorem 11B. These two propositions are called *dual theorems*
because they are equivalent. What we have noticed is that the theory
of isoperimetric problems admits of duality; that is, isoperimetric
theorems come in equivalent pairs.

The equivalence of (*) and (**) is demonstrated by the method
so often used above. For example, to show that (**) follows from (*),
we assume (*) is true and prove (**). Let F be any figure in C with
area A and perimeter P, let B_1 be the "blank" in C with area A and
perimeter P_1, and let B_2 be the "blank" in C with area A_2 and perimeter P. We shall prove that $P \geq P_1$. By (*), $A_2 \geq A$. Since all "blanks"
are similar and since the area of B_2 exceeds the area of B_1, the perimeter of B_2 exceeds the perimeter of B_1. Therefore, $P \geq P_1$. ▌ That
(**) implies (*) is just as easily proved.

2.3 Isoperimetric theorems for polygons

We next turn our attention to quadrilaterals and polygons in general. For brevity we call a polygon of n sides an n-gon. A regular n-gon is an n-gon with equal sides and equal angles. A natural question is: Of all n-gons with a given perimeter, which has the maximum area? It is reasonable to guess that the regular n-gon is the one. It turns out that it is just as difficult to verify this conjecture as to prove the Isoperimetric Theorem. Before examining it, therefore, we shall consider some simpler questions. For example, of all n-gons (n is fixed) inscribed in a given circle, which has the greatest area? For reasons of symmetry we might conjecture that again the regular n-gon is the one. (Could it be that there is no n-gon of greatest area which can be inscribed in the given circle, just as there is no regular polygon which has a greater number of sides than any other? Our intuition says no, and in this case it is truthful.) Having guessed the answer, we shall now prove it. To do so we shall use the method of Steiner given in the third proof of Theorem 11A above.

THEOREM 12. *Of all n-gons inscribed in a given circle, the regular n-gon has the greatest area.*

PROOF. We first observe that the proof of the theorem for $n = 3$ is in Chapter 4, where it is given as the solution to Problem 13. In the remainder of the proof of Theorem 12 we assume that n is greater than 3. Secondly, it should be emphasized that the various n-gons which may be inscribed in a circle have different perimeters as well as different areas.

Let R be a regular n-gon inscribed in a given circle Q with radius r, and denote the length of each side of R by s and the length of each

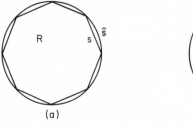
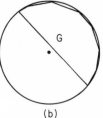

(a)   (b)

Figure 2.7

subtended arc by $\hat{s}$ [see Fig. 2.7(a)]. Since Q has circumference $2\pi r$,

$$\hat{s} = \frac{2\pi r}{n} \, .$$

Let G be any n-gon inscribed in Q. If the center of Q does not lie inside G [see Fig. 2.7(b)], then the area of G is certainly less than $\pi r^2/2$, since in this case G lies in one half of the circle. But a regular n-gon, $n > 3$, has a greater area than one half of its circumscribing circle as a computation shows. Consequently, the theorem is true if the center of Q does not lie inside of G. We henceforth assume that the center of Q does lie inside G.

The details of the remainder of the proof are numerous. Before you study them, read and think through the proof without paying attention to details, but note the main steps in the argument and convince yourself that, if these steps are correct, the desired conclusion is obtained. The main steps are three:

(1) Construction 1, which is a recipe for constructing an n-gon G_1 with the same sides and area as G, whose longest and shortest sides are adjacent, and which is inscribed in Q;

(2) Construction 2, which is a recipe for constructing an n-gon G_1' with at least one more side of length s than G has, with area greater than that of G and G_1, and which is inscribed in Q;

(3) Repeating these constructions over and over again.

Let us denote the lengths of the sides of G by a_i and the lengths of the corresponding subtended arcs by $\hat{a}_i$. If G is not regular, then it has at least one side of length less than s and at least one side of length greater than s. For, if

$$a_i \leq s \qquad\qquad (i = 1, \cdots, n),$$

then $a_i < s$ for at least one i, say $a_1 < s$, since otherwise G would be regular. But if

$$a_1 < s \quad \text{and} \quad a_i \leq s \qquad (i = 2, 3, \cdots, n),$$

then

$$\hat{a}_1 < \hat{s} \quad \text{and} \quad \hat{a}_i \leq \hat{s} \qquad (i = 2, 3, \cdots, n),$$

and consequently,

$$\hat{a}_1 + \hat{a}_2 + \cdots + \hat{a}_n < n\hat{s} = 2\pi r.$$

But $\hat{a}_1 + \hat{a}_2 + \cdots + \hat{a}_n = 2\pi r$, which is the circumference of Q.

Therefore, it cannot be that $a_i \leq s$ for each i from 1 to n. Similarly, it cannot be that $a_i \geq s$ for all i from 1 to n.

Construction 1. Suppose that the longest side of G has length a_n and that the shortest side has length a_1 ($a_1 < s < a_n$). We construct a new n-gon, G_1, by merely rearranging the order of G's sides in such a way that the longest side is adjacent to the shortest side; see Fig. 2.8.

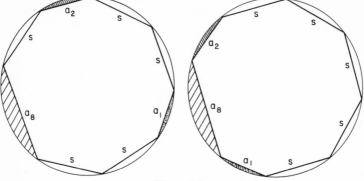

Figure 2.8

It is clear that the n-gon G_1 constructed in this way has the same area as G because the area of each is equal to that of Q minus that of the same pieces (the regions bounded by chords and subtended arcs in Fig. 2.8).

Next we construct another n-gon G_1', also inscribed in Q, and such that the area of G_1' is greater than that of G_1 and therefore is greater than that of G.

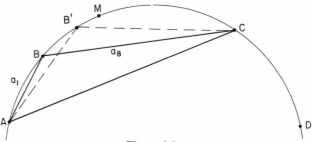

Figure 2.9

Construction 2. Consider the arcs AB and BC subtended by a_1 and a_n. Let us recall that $\hat{a}_1 < \hat{s}$ and $\hat{a}_n > \hat{s}$, and let us think of Fig. 2.9 as a magnified illustration of part of G_1 as seen in Fig. 2.8. Keep A

and C fixed and move B along the arc to a point B' so that $\widehat{AB'} = \hat{s}$. The n-gon G_1' is constructed to be the same as the n-gon G except that G_1' has B' as a vertex instead of B.

Consider the triangles ABC and $AB'C$. We shall now attempt to make it plausible that the area of $\triangle AB'C$ is greater than the area of $\triangle ABC$ by "demonstrating" that the altitude from B' is longer than that from B. It is reasonable to believe that the altitude increases as B approaches the midpoint M of ABC, so we shall limit ourselves to showing that B' is closer to M than B is, or that $\widehat{B'M} < \widehat{BM}$.

Since $\hat{a}_1 < \hat{s}$ and $\hat{a}_n > \hat{s}$, set

$$\hat{a}_1 = \hat{s} - h \quad \text{and} \quad \hat{a}_n = \hat{s} + k, \qquad h > 0, \quad k > 0.$$

But

$$\widehat{AM} = \tfrac{1}{2}(\hat{a}_1 + \hat{a}_n)$$

so that

$$\begin{aligned}
\widehat{BM} = \widehat{AM} - \widehat{AB} &= \tfrac{1}{2}(\hat{a}_1 + \hat{a}_n) - \hat{a}_1 \\
&= \tfrac{1}{2}(\hat{a}_n - \hat{a}_1) \\
&= \tfrac{1}{2}(\hat{s} + k - \hat{s} + h) \\
&= \tfrac{1}{2}(k + h),
\end{aligned}$$

and

$$\begin{aligned}
\widehat{B'M} = |\widehat{AM} - \widehat{AB'}| &= \tfrac{1}{2}|\hat{a}_1 + \hat{a}_n - 2\hat{s}| \\
&= \tfrac{1}{2}|\hat{s} - h + \hat{s} + k - 2\hat{s}| \\
&= \tfrac{1}{2}|k - h|.
\end{aligned}$$

Since k and h are positive, $|k - h| < k + h$. Therefore

$$\widehat{B'M} < \widehat{BM},$$

as we promised to show. While you may now believe that $\triangle AB'C$ has a longer altitude than $\triangle ABC$ and hence a greater area, you should realize that we have not proved it down to the last detail. A rigorous proof is provided by the fact that $|a - c| < |\overline{CB'} - s|$ and the following theorem: *Of two triangles on the same base (AC) and with the same vertex angle (equal to $\angle ABC$), the one with the smaller difference between the lengths of its legs has the longer altitude and the greater* *area.* (A proof of this theorem involves some of the steps in the solution to Problem 13, presented in Chapter 4, and modifications of others.)

We now have an n-gon G_1' inscribed in Q (with vertices A, B, C, etc.) which has a larger area than G and which has more sides of length s than G has (at least one more). The area of G_1' exceeds the area of G_1 since the area of $\triangle AB'C$ exceeds that of $\triangle ABC$ and since G_1' and G_1 coincide except along AB and BC and AB' and $B'C$. If G_1' is regular, there is nothing more to prove. If not, then we may repeat the previous constructions; and after employing them at most $n - 1$ times in all, we shall obtain a regular n-gon which is inscribed in the given circle and which has a larger area than G has. ∎

It is also possible to give an elementary proof of the isoperimetric theorem for quadrilaterals. (Elementary but not necessarily short and easy—an elementary proof is one which does not involve sophisticated advanced mathematics.)

THEOREM 13. *Of all quadrilaterals with a given area, the square has the least perimeter.*

It is easier to first prove the dual theorem—*Of all quadrilaterals with a given perimeter the square has the greatest area*—and then to deduce the desired conclusion.

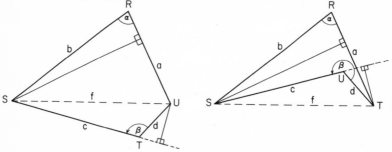

Figure 2.10

PROOF. We begin by deriving a formula for the area of a quadrilateral in terms of its sides and two opposite angles. Let a quadrilateral be given with consecutive sides a, b, c, and d in length and with area T and perimeter P. Suppose the first two sides include the angle α and the remaining two include the angle β. Let f be the length of the diagonal which "separates" the angles α and β. Then, since the altitude from D of triangle ADF has length $b \sin \alpha$ and that from F of triangle DBF has length $|\, d \sin \beta\,|$ (where for $\pi < \beta < 2\pi$, $\sin \beta$ is negative, see Fig. 2.10),

$$2T = ab \sin \alpha + cd \sin \beta,$$

from which it follows that

$$4T = 2ab \sin \alpha + 2cd \sin \beta$$

and

$$16T^2 = 4a^2b^2 \sin^2 \alpha + 8abcd \sin \alpha \sin \beta + 4c^2d^2 \sin^2 \beta.$$

We see by the law of cosines that

$$a^2 + b^2 - 2ab \cos \alpha = f^2 = c^2 + d^2 - 2cd \cos \beta$$

or

$$a^2 + b^2 - c^2 - d^2 = 2ab \cos \alpha - 2cd \cos \beta,$$

and

$$(a^2 + b^2 - c^2 - d^2)^2 = 4a^2b^2 \cos^2 \alpha - 8abcd \cos \alpha \cos \beta + 4c^2d^2 \cos^2 \beta.$$

We now add $16T^2$ and $(a^2 + b^2 - c^2 - d^2)^2$, and we obtain the formula

$$16T^2 + (a^2 + b^2 - c^2 - d^2)^2 = 4a^2b^2(\sin^2 \alpha + \cos^2 \alpha)$$
$$+ 4c^2d^2(\sin^2 \beta + \cos^2 \beta) - 8abcd\ (\cos \alpha \cos \beta - \sin \alpha \sin \beta).$$

But

$$\sin^2 x + \cos^2 x = 1,$$

and

$$\cos (x + y) = \cos x \cos y - \sin x \sin y$$

for all numbers x and y. Hence,

$$\text{(10)} \qquad \begin{aligned} 16T^2 + (a^2 + b^2 - c^2 - d^2)^2 \\ = 4a^2b^2 + 4c^2d^2 - 8\ abcd \cos (\alpha + \beta). \end{aligned}$$

If we temporarily assume a, b, c, and d to be fixed, then we see from (10) that T is largest when $\cos (\alpha + \beta)$ is smallest, that is, when $\cos (\alpha + \beta) = -1$. Hence, T is largest when $\alpha + \beta = \pi$. If $\alpha + \beta = \pi$, we may consider the quadrilateral with sides a, b, c, and d to be in-

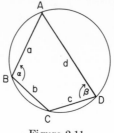

Figure 2.11

scribed in a circle (see Fig. 2.11); for, consider the circle determined
by the vertices A, B, and C. For all points D on the circle which are
not on the arc ABC, $\alpha + \beta = \pi$. If D is inside the circle,
then $\alpha + \beta > \pi$; and if D is outside the circle, $\alpha + \beta < \pi$ (we assume
that D does not lie on the arc ABC). We have thus proved

THEOREM 14. *A quadrilateral with given sides has the greatest area
when it can be inscribed in a circle.*

It remains to complete the proof of the dual of Theorem 13; that is,
it remains to show that among all quadrilaterals with given P whose
opposite angles add up to π, the square has the greatest area. We now
allow the lengths of the sides of the quadrilateral to vary although
we keep P fixed, and we keep the sum $\alpha + \beta$ equal to π. This means,
of course, that the radius of the circumscribing circle will also be per-
mitted to change. Now when $\alpha + \beta = \pi$, $\cos(\alpha + \beta) = -1$; and
we can rewrite equation (10) in the forms

$$16T^2 = 4(a^2b^2 + c^2d^2) + 8abcd - (a^2 + b^2 - c^2 - d^2)^2$$

$$= 4(ab + cd)^2 - (a^2 + b^2 - c^2 - d^2)^2$$

$$= [2(ab + cd) + (a^2 + b^2 - c^2 - d^2)]$$

$$\times [2(ab + cd) - (a^2 + b^2 - c^2 - d^2)]$$

$$= [(a + b)^2 - (c - d)^2][(c + d)^2 - (a - b)^2]$$

$$= [a + b + c - d][a + b - c + d]$$

$$\times [c + d + a - b][c + d - a + b]$$

or

$$(11) \quad 16T^2 = (P - 2a)(P - 2b)(P - 2c)(P - 2d).$$

This result should call Heron's formula sharply to mind and suggest strongly that we apply the Theorem of Arithmetic and Geometric Means (Theorem 8). If we do, we obtain the inequality

$$[(P - 2a)(P - 2b)(P - 2c)(P - 2d)]^{1/4}$$
$$\leq \frac{P - 2a + P - 2b + P - 2c + P - 2d}{4}$$

or

$$2T^{1/2} \leq \frac{P}{2}.$$

Equality holds if

$$P - 2a = P - 2b = P - 2c = P - 2d,$$

that is, if and only if $a = b = c = d$. Thus if we fix P, T is greatest when the inscribed quadrilateral is a square. All squares are similar; hence by duality, if we fix T, P is least when the quadrilateral is a square. ∎

In Section 1.2 we applied Theorem 8 to show that of all three-dimensional boxes with a given surface area, the cube has the greatest volume. The dual theorem is: *Of all right prisms with a rectangular base and having a given volume, the cube has the least surface area.* It and Theorem 13 enable us to prove a more general proposition concerning quadrilateral prisms. A quadrilateral prism is defined as follows. Let Q and Q' be two congruent quadrilaterals lying in two distinct parallel planes, and suppose that corresponding sides of Q and Q' are parallel. A *quadrilateral prism* is the solid formed by Q and Q' and all the line segments joining points of Q to corresponding points of Q'. If these line segments are perpendicular to the planes of Q and Q', the prism is said to be a *right prism*. Otherwise it is called an *oblique prism*. Q and Q' are called the *bases* of the prism, and the distance between their planes is the *altitude* of the prism. The volume of a prism is equal to the area of one of its bases times its altitude.

THEOREM 15. *Of all quadrilateral prisms with a given volume, the cube has the least surface area.*

PROOF. Let any quadrilateral prism P with surface area S be given. Whatever we may do to P, its volume V is to remain fixed. The proof has three main steps:

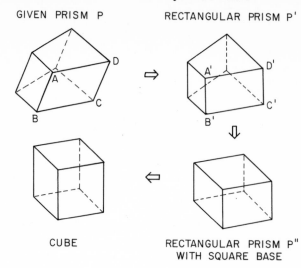

Figure 2.12

(1) Fixing the base of P, we transform it into a right prism. See Fig. 2.12.

(2) Keeping the area A of its base fixed, we transform the right prism with a quadrilateral base into a right prism with a square base.

(3) Lastly, we transform the right prism with a square base into a cube.

Now, if a right prism and an oblique prism have a common base and volume, the right prism has the smaller surface area. This is true because both prisms have the same altitude, say h, and because each lateral face of the right prism is a rectangle with altitude h, while the corresponding lateral face of the oblique prism is a parallelogram with altitude of at least length h and the same base as that of the rectangle (see Fig. 2.13). The areas of corresponding lateral faces are pairwise equal only if the given prism P is already a right prism. Thus step (1) cannot increase S. If the given prism P is not a right prism, then step (1) will actually decrease S.

Since both the area of the base and the altitude of the right prism are kept fixed during step (2), and since the lateral surface area of a right prism is equal to its altitude multiplied by the perimeter of its base, it is a consequence of Theorem 13 that step (2) again cannot increase S. Unless the base of the right prism is a square, S will actually be decreased as a result of step (2).

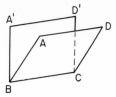

Figure 2.13

Finally, by the dual theorem stated on page 51, step (3) cannot increase S and will, in fact, decrease it unless the right prism with a square base is already a cube. Therefore, unless P is a cube, S will actually diminish during at least one of the three transformations of P. ∎

PROBLEM 15. Given the sum of the areas of five faces of a box (rectangular parallelepiped with one face removed), find the box of maximum possible volume.

PROBLEM 16. The girth of a box is twice its width plus twice its height. Of all boxes whose length and girth combined do not exceed L inches, which has the maximum volume?
A frequent parcel post user would do well to be familiar with the solution to this problem.

PROBLEM 17. The sum of the lengths of the edges of a box is given. Show that of all such boxes, the cube has the greatest volume and surface area.

PROBLEM 18. Assuming that of all tetrahedra with volume V there is one with the least surface area, show that the regular tetrahedron is that one.

PROBLEM 19. An octahedron composed of two congruent pyramids joined together at their square bases may be called a double pyramid with a square base. Show that of all right double pyramids with a square base and volume V, the regular octahedron has the least surface area. Extend the theorem to the class of all double pyramids with square bases.

Having proved the isoperimetric theorem for triangles and quadrilaterals, we might be so encouraged as to believe that we could prove corresponding theorems for pentagons, hexagons, and even for polygons in general. Unfortunately, it seems at present that this cannot be done without the use of the Isoperimetric Theorem itself or its equivalent.

Before we proceed any further, it might be well to define carefully what is meant by a *plane polygon*. A plane polygon is made up of a finite number of straight-line segments all of which lie in the same plane. These line segments are called *sides* of the polygon and their endpoints are called *vertices* of the polygon. A plane polygon is defined by the condition that each vertex must be the endpoint of at least two sides and that the only points lying on more than one side are vertices. If each vertex of a plane polygon is the endpoint of exactly two sides, then the plane polygon is called a *simple* plane polygon. All the polygons we shall consider are simple plane polygons. We shall continue to refer to a simple plane polygon simply as a polygon. The region inside a polygon is called its *interior*. (People often refer to a polygon together with its interior as a polygon.)

THEOREM 16. *Given any n-gon which does not have all its sides of equal length, one can construct another n-gon with the same perimeter, with all sides of equal length, and with a larger area.*

A false proof of this theorem is given below, one which the author designed and with which he once deceived himself. It is based upon Theorem 12. Read it carefully, and see if you can discover where it is incorrect or incomplete.

PROOF. Let the given n-gon G have perimeter P. Since its sides are not all of length P/n, it must have at least one side of greater length than P/n and one of smaller length. Our first task is to show that we may assume these two sides to be adjacent. When we have done this, we shall complete the proof by using a slightly modified version of the demonstration of Theorem 12.

Suppose G has no pair of adjacent sides with one longer than P/n and one shorter. Then it must be that there are k consecutive sides ($k \geq 1$) of length P/n which separate such a pair. Let the short side be AB and the long side be XY. If the segment AC lies inside G, we can reflect the triangle ABC using the perpendicular bisector of AC as a two sided mirror and obtain a new n-gon $AB'CD\cdots$ with the same sides as G and with the same area (see Fig. 2.14). If AC does not lie in G, then we first reflect the triangle ABC in the line AC and obtain an n-gon with the same sides as G but with a greater area. AC will lie inside the new n-gon, and we now reflect in the perpendicular bisector of AC as before. We next repeat this process with B', C, and D taking the roles of A, B, and C, respectively. After exactly k such steps, we shall have obtained an n-gon with the same sides as G, with at least as great an area, and with a pair of adjacent sides, one of which is shorter than P/n and one of which is longer. Let them be called AB and BC, respectively. We may suppose that AC is interior to the n-gon.

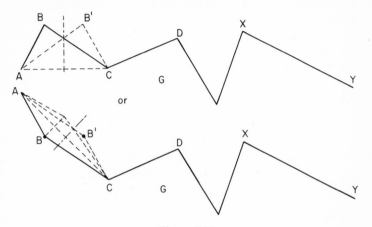

Figure 2.14

We now construct $AB'C$ with $\overline{AB'} = P/n$ and
$$\overline{AB'} + \overline{B'C} = \overline{AB} + \overline{BC},$$

and we show that the area T' of $\triangle AB'C$ is greater than the area T of $\triangle ABC$. We know, because of our construction, that
$$\overline{AB'} + \overline{B'C} = \overline{AB} + \overline{BC}$$

and that
$$\overline{AB} < \overline{AB'} = \frac{P}{n} < \overline{BC}.$$

Hence
$$\overline{BC} - \overline{AB} > \overline{BC} - \overline{AB'}.$$

Moreover,
$$\overline{B'C} = \overline{AB} + \overline{BC} - \overline{AB'} < \overline{AB} + \overline{BC} - \overline{AB} = \overline{BC}.$$

Finally,
$$\overline{BC} - \overline{AB} > \overline{BC} - \overline{AB'} > \overline{B'C} - \overline{AB'}.$$

Using Heron's formula [see (7), page 35], we conclude that

$$16T^2 = [(\overline{AB} + \overline{BC})^2 - \overline{AC}^2] \cdot [\overline{AC}^2 - (\overline{BC} - \overline{AB})^2].$$

To compare T and T', we observe that the first factor is the same for both triangles while, according to the last inequality, the second factor is greater for the triangle $AB'C$ than for ABC; therefore $T' > T$. Hence, the area of the n-gon $AB'C\cdots$ is greater than the area of the n-gon $ABC\cdots$. By construction the two n-gons have the same perimeter.

If we repeat this argument at most $n - 1$ times, we shall obtain an n-gon with perimeter P and with equal sides. It will have an area greater than that of G. ∎

The error in this "proof" lies in the reflection steps. It may very well be that the triangle ABC, for example, cannot be reflected in the perpendicular bisector of AC without AB' intersecting CD (see Fig. 2.15), something which we cannot allow to happen. This reflection can be performed without such a difficulty provided G is convex.

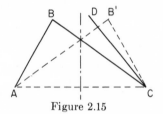
Figure 2.15

DEFINITION 5. A plane figure is *convex* if the straight line segments joining pairs of points of the figure all lie entirely within the figure.

If a figure is not convex, then there is at least one pair of points of the figure such that the line segment joining them lies outside the figure except for its endpoints.

If G is not convex, one might hope to be able to find another n-gon which is convex, which has the same sides in the same order, and which has a larger area, by a finite number of reflection operations of the following kind. Suppose all points of the line segment joining two nonconsecutive vertices, say A and B, of G lie outside of G, except for A and B. A reflection operation consists in reflecting the part of the boundary of G lying between A and B in AB (see Fig. 2.16).

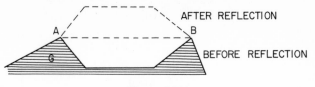

Figure 2.16

QUESTION. Given an n-gon, G, can one construct, with a finite number of reflection operations, a convex n-gon G' having the same sides in the same order as G?

Theorem 16 can be proved either by demonstrating that the answer to this question is yes, which it is, or by using the following argument. Join each pair of vertices of G by a straight-line segment. Delete those segments that lie in the interior of some polygon. The remaining line segments constitute a convex polygon called the *convex hull* of G. Clearly it has a smaller perimeter and larger area than G unless it coincides with G. The polygon of perimeter P which is similar to the convex hull of G can now be transformed using the argument in the false proof above, and Theorem 16 is proved. The only objection one might have to this argument is that the convex hull of G might have fewer than n sides. However, by adding a few pseudo-vertices on the interiors of sides one can consider the convex hull to be an n-gon.

Another theorem which we cannot easily prove is: *The regular n-gon has the greatest area of all n-gons with equal sides and the same perimeter.* This is unfortunate in view of the following soluble problem.

PROBLEM 20. Show that a circle has a greater area than a regular n-gon with the same perimeter.
Hint. Inscribe a circle in the regular n-gon. Suppose its radius is r and that the n-gon has perimeter P and area A. Show that

$$A = \frac{P^2 r^2}{4A} < \frac{P^2}{4\pi}.$$

For, if we could prove this theorem, then using the result of Problem 20, we could prove that: *A circle has a greater area than any polygon with the same perimeter.* This would be a significant accomplishment.

The argument is as follows. Let S be any polygon, and let C be a circle having the same perimeter P as S. By Theorem 16, we can construct a second polygon S' with all sides of equal length, with perimeter P, and with area T' greater than the area T of S. *If* a regular polygon S'' having perimeter P has an area $T'' > T'$, then by the result of Problem 20 the area of C is greater than T'', and hence greater than T. As we have remarked, the "if" in this argument is not easily removed.

2.4 Steiner's attempt

Before we describe one of Steiner's attempted proofs of the Iso-perimetric Theorem, we should emphasize some points involved in each of the proofs of isoperimetric theorems for polygons which we have given.

In the first place, we have always proceeded constructively; that is, in proving a theorem we have never argued that if the theorem were false, a conclusion would follow which contradicts the hypothesis of the theorem, hence the theorem must be correct. A proof which is based on such an argument is often called an *indirect proof*. Indirect proofs are *nonconstructive*. Our problem has been to show that a certain figure is an *extremal* figure among a certain class of figures, that is, that its area (or whatever property is under consideration) is greater or less than that of any other figure in the class. By geo-metric construction, we have always been able to demonstrate that the conjectured extremal figure has the desired property.

In the second place, it is important to realize that it is not always possible to give such an explicit demonstration. Indeed, it may be that no extremal figure exists in the class of allowed figures. Merely to show that any figure which is not the supposed extremal figure can be improved is not sufficient argument to complete a proof that the supposed extremum is indeed one. Also, we might not be sufficiently clever to conjecture a solution to a given problem, although we might be most curious as to its solution. Let us consider some specific exam-ples illustrating these statements.

QUESTION. Which fraction of the form $1/n$ $(n = 1, 2, 3, \cdots)$ is the smallest?

PROPOSED SOLUTION. For each fraction of the form $1/n$, except the fraction $1/1$, there is another fraction $1/n^2$ which has the same form and which is smaller; that is,

$$\frac{1}{n^2} < \frac{1}{n} \quad \text{if} \quad n > 1.$$

Therefore, 1/1 is the smallest fraction in the given collection of fractions. ∎

This solution is obviously false; and, in fact, there is no smallest fraction in the given class. We have found a number which, with respect to the operation of squaring, is the only one of the allowed numbers which cannot be decreased. Conceivably, all the other operations we could think of would also have this property. But, as we have just observed, this is not sufficient to show that 1 is the smallest of the allowed numbers.

QUESTION. Which is the surface of least area which
(A) is bounded by the circumference C of a horizontal circular disc of unit radius,
(B) passes through a point P one unit above the center of the disc,
(C) is such that no vertical line cuts the surface in more than one point?

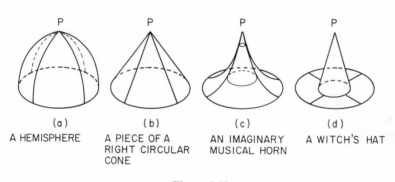

(a)   (b)   (c)   (d)
A HEMISPHERE   A PIECE OF A   AN IMAGINARY   A WITCH'S HAT
                RIGHT CIRCULAR   MUSICAL HORN
                CONE

Figure 2.17

Some possible surfaces are illustrated in Fig. 2.17. Remember, the circular disc is not part of any of them. Again, there is no extremal. To prove this, first observe that the minimal surface, if it exists, must have area greater than π, the area of the disc. But given any surface satisfying the three specified conditions and having area $S = \pi + h$, we can construct a surface consisting of (1) a thin "ice cream cone" whose vertex is P and whose base lies in the disc bounded by C and of (2) that portion of the disc which lies outside the base of the cone, and such that the area of this surface is less than $\pi + h$ [see Fig. 2.17(d)]. For let the radius of the base of the cone be r. Then the area of the surface is the sum $\pi - \pi r^2 + \pi r \sqrt{r^2 + 1}$ of the area $\pi - \pi r^2$ of the annulus† and the area $\pi r \sqrt{r^2 + 1}$ of the ice cream cone. Moreover, $\pi r \sqrt{r^2 + 1} - \pi r^2$, which is equal to $\pi r (\sqrt{r^2 + 1} - r)$, can certainly be made less than h by taking r small enough. If we eliminate condition (B), thereby widening the class of allowed surfaces, then in the new class of surfaces there is a minimal surface, the disc.

Thus sometimes we can widen the class of allowed figures and thereby solve a problem for which no extremal figure existed previously (as in the above example and in case of the isoperimetric theorem for any figure with area T instead of any polygon with area T); and sometimes by restricting the class of allowed figures we can do the same thing (as in the case of the isoperimetric problem restricted to triangles instead of polygons in general with area T).

Perhaps you have noticed that I have not referred to problems for which no extremal figure exists as "problems with no solution" or "no answer." In cases of this sort, I prefer to say that no extremal figure of the desired kind exists but that, since this is known, the problem has been solved.

Note. Perhaps the reader knows that, considering only surface tension, a soap film formed on a wire frame takes the shape of the surface of least area among all those bounded by the frame. For an interesting discussion of soap films and minimal surfaces, read pages 385–397 in *What is Mathematics?* by Courant and Robbins, Oxford University Press, New York, 1941.

Our intuition does not always advise us correctly. How do you think the following question might be answered? Draw some pictures before you make a conjecture.

QUESTION. Of all closed curves inside of which one can move a line segment 1 unit long so that it makes a full turn of 360°, which encloses the least area? Or, colloquially speaking, what is the shape of the parking lot of least area [or a parking lot of least area (there might be least ones of many different shapes, all with the same area)] on which a super-streamlined car of unit length can be turned around?

A circle of unit diameter is a possibility. Will a curve enclosing less area do the job? A. S. Besicovitch was able to prove that there is no such closed curve enclosing the least area. What is more astounding, he proved that for any positive number p, no matter how small, there is a closed curve having the desired property which encloses less than

† An *annulus* is a plane figure bounded by two concentric circles, that is, a circle with a circular hole in the middle.

p square units of area! One can move a line segment 1 unit long so that it turns completely about but sweeps out only 1/10 of a sq. unit of area in the process. If we had remarkably delicate instruments, we could do the job using only 10^{-10} sq. units of area!

If we restrict the class of allowed figures by imposing the additional condition that they be convex, then an extremal curve does exist. It is the equilateral triangle of altitude 1 unit (see Fig. 2.18). For a solution and discussion of this problem and many other beautiful problems concerning convex figures, read the book *Plane Convex Figures* by the Russian mathematicians I. M. Yaglom and V. G. Boltyanskiĭ (German translation published by VEB Deutscher Verlag der Wissenschaften, Berlin, 1956), English translation published by Holt, Rinehart, and Winston, Inc., New York, 1961.

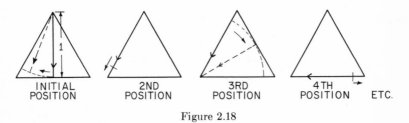

Figure 2.18

The difficulty in proving the Isoperimetric Theorem is of the same sort as in the examples cited above, only in this case an extremal figure does exist. It is relatively easy to show that for any plane figure which is not a circle, there is another with the same perimeter but with a larger area. This is not enough to prove the Isoperimetric Theorem. This argument tells us only that, *if* there is a figure which has a greater area than any other figure with the same perimeter, then it must be the circle. It is altogether conceivable that there is no such extremal figure. Steiner did not believe that the point we are now discussing was too serious. After all, it is obvious to the geometric intuition that a solution to the Isoperimetric Problem does exist and that it is the circle. Fortunately for modern mathematics, Weierstrass did believe that he had raised a serious objection to Steiner's proofs of the Isoperimetric Theorem by calling attention to this point; and in fact, he believed that his argument rendered Steiner's proofs (and also other proofs of other theorems) invalid. He overcame his own objection by supplying, in a nonconstructive way, an existence proof of the solution of the Isoperimetric Problem. And no one has yet found a simple geometrical argument to show that the circle has a greater area than any other figure with the same perimeter. None is expected to be found. All proofs of the Isoperimetric Theorem show, in a nonconstructive way, that a figure of maximum area does exist.

While Steiner did not prove the Isoperimetric Theorem, the reasoning he used in attempting proofs is beautiful and ingenious. We now consider one of his attempted proofs and demonstrate that: *For any plane figure which is not a circle there is another with greater area and with the same perimeter.*

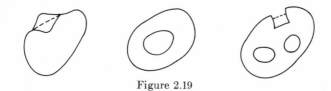

Figure 2.19

Let a plane figure with perimeter P be given, and suppose that it is not a circle. If it is not convex, we construct another figure with perimeter P but with a larger area as follows. We pick two points on the boundary of the figure such that the line segment joining them lies outside the figure, and we reflect that area between this line segment and the figure in the line segment as a mirror (see Fig. 2.19). We choose the new figure to be the original one plus the area reflected and its reflection. This new figure has the same perimeter but a larger area. This argument really doesn't take care of all possible cases as the diagrams in Fig. 2.19 show, but it is easy to take care of the exceptions indicated. Try it.

If the given figure is convex, we take advantage of Theorem 14. Since the figure is not a circle, there must exist four points on its boundary which are not the vertices of a convex quadrilateral inscribed in a circle. Let us consider the convex quadrilateral whose vertices are these four points. Let us assume that the parts of the figure exterior to this quadrilateral (see shaded regions in Fig. 2.20) are fixed in shape and area and rigidly attached to the sides of the quadrilateral. Let us also consider the quadrilateral to have flexible joints at its vertices. By Theorem 14, if we now distort the quadrilateral until it is inscribable in a circle, we shall have increased its area. The new quadrilateral together with the pieces of the original figure rigidly attached to it (see Fig. 2.20) determines a new figure with perimeter P but with a greater area than that of the original figure. This completes Steiner's argument.

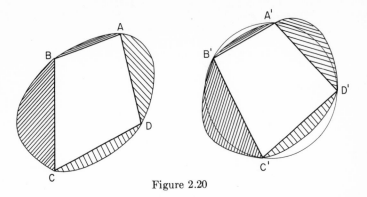

Figure 2.20

PROBLEM 21. Show that the Isoperimetric Theorem implies that, of all n-gons with the same sides, the one which can be inscribed in a circle has the greatest area.

Using the result of this problem, we can prove that: *Of all n-gons with the same perimeter, the regular n-gon has the greatest area.*

PROOF. Let G be any irregular n-gon. By the result of Problem 21 the n-gon G', which has the same sides as G in the same order and which can be inscribed in a circle, has a larger area. Since G' is inscribed in a circle, we may rearrange its sides in any order we please. Noting this fact, we can use the last half of the false proof of Theorem 16 to reach the desired conclusion. ▮

There is still another form in which we can state the Isoperimetric Theorem. Let A denote the area and P the perimeter of a given figure, and suppose that the circle of perimeter P has radius r. Then the theorem is equivalent to the inequality

$$A \leq \pi r^2;$$

or since $r = P/2\pi$,

$$\frac{4\pi A}{P^2} \leq 1.$$

This inequality is called the *isoperimetric inequality*. The quotient $4\pi A/P^2$ is called the *isoperimetric quotient* by G. Pólya. Following him, we abbreviate "isoperimetric quotient" by "I.Q." and state the Isoperimetric Theorem in the following form: *Of all plane figures, the circle has the highest I.Q.*

PROBLEM 22. Compute the I.Q. of several figures. Do the data obtained support the theorem?

CHAPTER THREE

The Reflection Principle

3.1 Symmetry

"Symmetry, as wide or as narrow as you may define its meaning, is one idea by which man through the ages has tried to comprehend and create order, beauty and perfection." Thus wrote Hermann Weyl, one of the great mathematicians of our time.† Indeed, arguments based upon notions of symmetry are among the most powerful and elegant in mathematics. In this chapter we shall examine the role played in the study of inequalities by the simplest kind of symmetry which a plane figure can possess, namely, symmetry with respect to a line (which divides the figure into two parts, each the mirror image of the other). Symmetry strongly influenced the art of early civilizations. Its use in mathematics was begun by the Greeks. It led them to their wonderful discoveries of regular polyhedra: tetrahedron, cube, octahedron, dodecahedron, and icosahedron. In turn, the symmetries of polyhedra have been partially responsible for the creation of the branch of modern mathematics known as algebraic topology. For an introduction to this point of view, I highly recommend that you read the book *Geometry and the Imagination* by David Hilbert and S. Cohn-Vossen, Chelsea Press, New York, 1952.

† This is a quotation from his lovely book, *Symmetry*, Princeton University Press, 1952.

Symmetry is aesthetically pleasing, and many wonderful geometric figures can be found through constructions that involve reflections, for example, constructions of regular polyhedra (read the discussion by Hilbert and Cohn-Vossen). However, it is the abstract mathematical principle which is associated with the concept of reflection that we shall have occasion to use most often. The discovery of this abstraction, known as the *Reflection Principle*, is credited to Heron. He found that *a ray of light reflected from a plane takes the shortest possible path between the source and the receiver.* Equivalent to this principle is the fact that, *for a ray reflected by a plane surface, the angle of incidence equals the angle of reflection.* In case you are unfamiliar with a proof of this equivalence, one is presented below.

Suppose A is the source, B is the receiver, and m is the reflector (see Fig. 3.1). We first assume that ACB is a path with equal angles of incidence and reflection and prove that it is the shortest path from A to m to B. Let B' be the reflection of B in m. Then $\measuredangle ACX = \measuredangle BCY = \measuredangle B'CY$; and hence, ACB' is a straight-line segment, the shortest path from A to B'. But $\overline{BC} = \overline{B'C}$; and in fact, $\overline{BP} = \overline{B'P}$ for any point P on m. That is,

$$\overline{AP} + \overline{PB} = \overline{AP} + \overline{PB'} > \overline{AC} + \overline{CB'} = \overline{AC} + \overline{CB}.$$

Therefore, ACB is the shortest path from A to m to B. The converse of this theorem follows from the congruence $\triangle BCP \cong \triangle B'CP$ and the equality $\measuredangle ACX = \measuredangle B'CP$. ∎

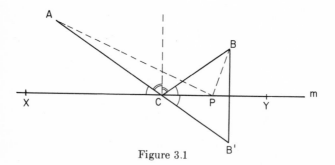

Figure 3.1

Although the reflection principle is both simple and obvious, it makes clear, when used in the right place, what is otherwise opaque or nearly so. I shall try to give some illustrations of this fact, but first let us examine some ideas based upon simple reflection.

3.2 Dido's problem

Simple reflection was used to great effect by Steiner in connection with the Isoperimetric Theorem and its consequences. One consequence is the solution to Dido's problem. Dido was the daughter of a Tyrian king. According to legend, she was married to her uncle, Acerbas, who was murdered for the sake of his wealth. Dido then fled to Cyprus with Acerbas' treasure and sailed from there to the coast of Africa near Sicily. She told the local ruler that she would like to purchase some land along the seashore, a piece not larger than an oxhide can surround. He consented to this small request from a beautiful lady and generously provided her with a large hide. The clever Dido then cut the hide into thin strips and tied their ends together to form a rope so as to be able to surround considerably more land than the ruler had imagined. If we assume the seashore to be a straight line and the earth to be flat, she was next faced with the problem: What is the figure of maximum area which can be surrounded by a string of given length and an unspecified portion of a straight line? Dido solved the problem, and partly due to her successful solution, became the founder and queen of the prosperous city of Carthage.

As we mentioned, the solution to Dido's problem lies in reflection. If we think of the seashore as a mirror in which we reflect the region surrounded by the hide rope, her problem becomes: What is the figure of maximum area having a given line of symmetry (the seashore) and a given perimeter (twice the length of the rope)? Since the class of all figures with a given perimeter includes those which also have an axis of symmetry, and since the circle has an axis of symmetry, the Isoperimetric Theorem guarantees that the circle is the desired figure of maximum area; hence, the solution to Dido's problem is a semicircle.

PROBLEM 23. Which is the figure of maximum area bounded by a string of length L and a stick of length D if $L > D$? Give a proof.

PROBLEM 24. The order and lengths of all but one of the sides of an n-gon are given. Which such n-gon has the greatest area? Prove your conjecture.

PROBLEM 25. Given a quarter of a plane, which is the figure of largest area which can be cut off from it by a curve of given length? Generalize your result.

Hint. Reflect more than once.

PROBLEM 26. Generalize Problem 23 to three dimensions and solve the new problem.

3.3 Steiner symmetrization

Assuming that there is a figure of maximum area among those with a given perimeter, one can also use reflection to prove the Isoperimetric Theorem. Steiner devised several proofs of this kind. One of his ideas was to prove that *the maximal figure must be symmetric with respect to every line which divides its perimeter into two equal parts.*

To prove this, we observe that the maximal figure must be convex and confine further discussion to convex figures. Now, a chord which divides the perimeter of a convex body into equal parts lies entirely within the body. If there exists such a chord which does not divide the area of the body into equal halves, then we can remove the half with smaller area, and replace it by the mirror image of the larger half. We thus obtain a new figure with a larger area but having the same perimeter as the original one. This new figure may not be convex. In this case we can make it convex (see Section 2.4) thus increasing the area and leaving the perimeter fixed. Note also that a chord which divides the perimeter in half may divide a convex body into halves of equal area which are not symmetric with respect to the chord. In this case it makes no difference which half is selected for reflection. Again, the resulting figure may not be convex, but it can be made convex as before. Consequently, if it exists, the plane figure of greatest area which has a given perimeter must be symmetric with respect to every line which divides its perimeter into equal halves and must therefore be a circle. (This last "must" needs substantiation.) ▌

Another of Steiner's proofs of the Isoperimetric Theorem is based in a different way upon the idea that *the maximal figure must have an axis of symmetry in every direction.* To describe this idea, let us first call attention to a theorem on trapezoids. Suppose $ABCD$ is a trapezoid, and suppose $AB'C'D$ is an isosceles trapezoid with the same bases and altitude; that is, suppose $AB'C'D$ is symmetric with respect to the perpendicular bisector of AD. It is but a rewording of the Reflection Principle to say that the perimeter of a triangle having a given base and altitude is least when it is isosceles. (See Fig. 3.2(d), where A may be considered the source, D the receiver, and $B'C'$ the mirror.) Thus the area of $AB'C'D$ is equal to the area of $ABCD$, while its perimeter is less than or equal to the perimeter of $ABCD$.

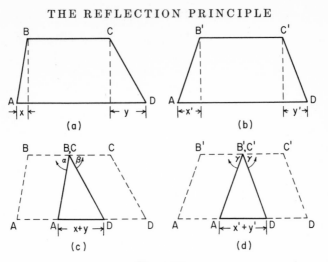

Figure 3.2

Now consider any convex body [Fig. 3.3(a)]. Let us slice it into thin strips whose sides are parallel; and, for the moment, let us assume each strip to be a trapezoid [Fig. 3.3(b)]. From these trapezoids we construct a new figure by transforming each one into an isosceles trapezoid with the same bases and area and by then lining up the new trapezoids so that they have a common perpendicular bisector [Fig. 3.3(c)]. It follows from the above theorem on trapezoids that Fig. 3.3(c) has the same area as Fig. 3.3(b) but a smaller perimeter. If we divide the original convex body [Fig. 3.3(a)] into thinner and thinner strips, the approximating polygons [Fig. 3.3(b)] will have areas and perimeters approaching those of the original figure. (In

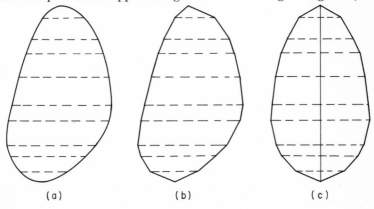

Figure 3.3

fact, one often defines the area and perimeter of a plane figure to be
the respective limits of the areas and perimeters of a sequence of
approximating polygons.) The transformed polygons [Fig. 3.3(c)]
will approach a convex body with an axis of symmetry. Thus, *given
a convex body, we can construct another with the same area, no greater
perimeter, and with an axis of symmetry in a given direction.* (Can you
prove that the symmetrized figure is indeed convex?) This symmetric
convex body may also be thought of as being obtained by the following construction.

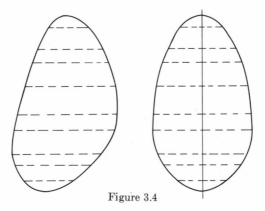

Figure 3.4

Construction. Draw a straight line in the direction given, and consider the chords of the original convex body which are perpendicular
to the drawn line. Move each such chord so that the drawn line becomes its perpendicular bisector.

The endpoints of the translated chords form a new symmetric
figure (see Fig. 3.4), with the same area as the original one but with a
smaller perimeter. This construction is called *Steiner symmetrization.*
It plays an important role in the theory of convex bodies.

We are now in a position to complete our "proof" of the Isoperimetric Theorem. Given a convex body which does not have an axis of
symmetry in some direction, we apply a Steiner symmetrization to it
with respect to that direction; and we obtain a new convex body with
the same area and a smaller perimeter. Then we magnify the new
body until its perimeter is the same as that of the original body. Thus,
if a figure does not have an axis of symmetry in every direction, it
cannot be the figure of largest area among all those with the same
perimeter. It follows that, if a maximal figure exists, the circle is the
maximal figure. (The proof of the last statement is left to the reader.)

3.4 Conic sections

In this section we shall wander from the subject of inequalities for a short time and consider some geometric objects for their own sake: the ellipse, parabola, and hyperbola. These plane curves are known as the *conic sections*, and they are so called because they are all curves of intersection of a right circular cone and a plane. A right circular cone is defined as follows: Let C be a circle, and let V be a point on that line which is perpendicular to the plane of the circle and which passes through its center O (see Fig. 3.5). If V is not O, all the straight lines passing through V and points of C form a surface which is called a *right circular cone*. The line through V and O is its *axis*, and the point V is its *vertex*.

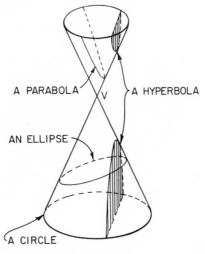

Figure 3.5

The curve of intersection of the cone and a plane perpendicular to its axis is clearly a circle. When the intersecting plane is inclined slightly from the perpendicular position, the curve of intersection is no longer a circle, but it is still a closed curve. Any closed curve which is the curve of intersection of a plane with a right circular cone is called an *ellipse*. Thus, a circle is a special ellipse. Of course, not all ellipses are circles. An ellipse plus its interior is convex because each half of a right circular cone plus its interior is convex. As the plane is inclined more and more, the ellipses formed by it and the cone become more and more elongated. When the plane is parallel to one of the lines making up the surface of the cone, the curve of intersection is no longer a closed convex curve but is a curve of infinite length, namely a *parabola*. If the plane is inclined still further, the curve of intersection will still be of infinite length but will have two separate branches. This conic section is defined to be a *hyperbola*.

Another way of characterizing the ellipse is this: *An ellipse is a plane curve such that for each point on the curve the sum of its distances to two fixed points is the same.* Thus if one pins one end of a thread to a point F_1 and the other end to a point F_2 on a flat sheet of paper and draws an arc by moving a pencil so as to keep the thread taut and flat on the paper, the arc will be a portion of an ellipse (see Fig. 3.6).

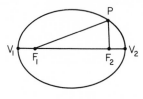

Figure 3.6

The connection between this definition of the ellipse and its definition as a conic section is easily established, although this is rarely done in mathematics courses where the ellipse is discussed. We shall prove that *the ellipse defined as a conic section has the property described by the figure above.* Afterwards, we shall return to the subject of inequalities and use the Reflection Principle to establish another important property of the ellipse.

PROOF. (A Belgian mathematician, Dandelin (1794–1847), had this ingenious, beautiful idea.) Consider Fig. 3.7 which illustrates an ellipse drawn on a right circular cone. We construct two spheres lying inside the cone both of which are tangent to the cone and to the plane of the ellipse. One sphere is above this plane and one is below it. Let the points of tangency between the plane and the spheres be F_1 and F_2, and let P be any point on the ellipse. Consider the straight-line segment VP_1PP_2 on the surface of the cone, where V denotes its vertex and where P_1 and P_2 are points of tangency between the line segment and the spheres. Since PP_1 and PF_1 are segments of tangents to the upper sphere which are drawn from the same point,

$$\overline{PF}_1 = \overline{PP}_1.$$

Similarly,

$$\overline{PF}_2 = \overline{PP}_2.$$

Therefore,

$$\overline{PF_1} + \overline{PF_2} = \overline{P_1P} + \overline{PP_2} = \overline{P_1P_2}.$$

But $\overline{P_1P_2}$ is a constant independent of P. (Why?) Hence, $\overline{PF_2} + \overline{PF_1}$ is a constant, and we see that an ellipse is a curve which is the locus of points in a plane the sums of whose distances to two fixed points in the plane are all equal. ∎

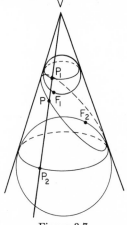

Figure 3.7

We shall have occasion to use later the following property of an ellipse: It is the locus of the vertex P of a triangle F_1PF_2 with fixed base $2c = \overline{F_1F_2}$ and fixed perimeter $p > 4c$. Any triangle $F_1P'F_2$ whose vertex P' lies inside the ellipse has a perimeter less than p, and any triangle $F_1P'F_2$ whose vertex P' lies outside the ellipse has a perimeter greater than p.

It can be shown similarly that a hyperbola is a locus of points in the plane the differences of whose distances to two fixed points are all equal. (Two tangent spheres are constructed on the same side of the plane of the hyperbola.)

PROBLEM 27. Draw a figure and complete the demonstration of this property of the hyperbola.

The two fixed points mentioned in the above characterizations of the ellipse and hyperbola are called *foci*. "Focus" is a Latin word meaning a *hearth*, that is, a place where things are burned. (The plural of "focus" is "foci," and the "c" in "foci" is pronounced as an "s.") To see why the focus of an ellipse is a burning place, we use the Reflection Principle. Let l be a tangent to an ellipse with foci F_1 and F_2 ; see

Fig. 3.8. Let P be the point of tangency, and suppose that Q is any other point on l. Since Q is outside the ellipse,

$$\overline{QF_1} + \overline{QF_2} > \overline{PF_1} + \overline{PF_2}.$$

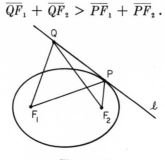

Figure 3.8

Therefore, F_1PF_2 is the shortest path from F_1 to l to F_2, and the Reflection Principle thus tells us that the focal radii PF_1 and PF_2 make equal angles with the tangent l. This means that if the ellipse were a reflector, rays from a point source of light at F_1 would all be focused at F_2 by the ellipse; a focus is indeed a "burning place."

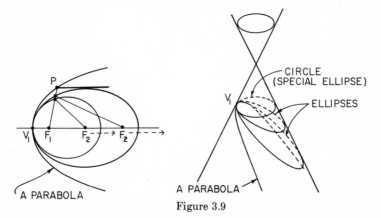

Figure 3.9

The *vertices* of an ellipse are the endpoints of the longest chord of the ellipse, and this chord passes through the foci. If one focus of the ellipse, say F_1, is fixed along with the closest vertex V_1, and if the other focus moves farther and farther away along the line through V_1 and F_1, then the ellipse becomes increasingly elongated and finally, in the limit, becomes a parabola (see Fig. 3.9). In the limit, the focal radius PF_2 is parallel to the axis, that is, the line through V_1 and F_1. This property of the parabola, that it reflects all rays emanating from its focus in the same direction, is used, of course, in the design of such diverse instruments as automobile headlights and radio telescopes.

PROBLEM 28. Show that a tangent to a hyperbola bisects the angle made by the focal radii from the point of tangency.

Hint. Let l be the line which bisects angle F_1TF_2 (see Fig. 3.10), and show that T is the only point of l which lies on the hyperbola by proving that, for any other point P on l, $\overline{PF_1} - \overline{PF_2} < \overline{TF_1} - \overline{TF_2}$. Use reflection in l.

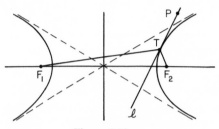

Figure 3.10

An ellipse and a hyperbola are said to be *confocal* if they have the same foci.

PROBLEM 29. Prove that if an ellipse and a hyperbola are confocal, then at any point where they intersect their tangents are perpendicular.

3.5 Triangles

Arguments based upon the geometrical notion of reflection are often unexpectedly helpful. Many problems resist the most strenuous efforts directed at their solution; yet once one has the idea "try reflection," they yield and become charmingly simple. This is especially so with respect to properties of triangles. Triangles have been studied for thousands of years, but new properties of triangles appear every now and then. Some of them are only conjectured. That is, there is substantial evidence supporting them, but no one has been able to prove that they are true. In this section we shall examine some of the more recently discovered properties of triangles.

We begin with Fagnano's Problem (see Fig. 3.11): *What is the triangle of minimum perimeter which can be inscribed in a given acute-angled triangle?* Can you guess the solution? What does the Reflection Principle tell you? Take some time, examine some special cases, and see if you can formulate a conjecture.

The solution of Fagnano's Problem, which is given below, is due to the famous Hungarian mathematician L. Fejér (1880–1958). He found it in 1900 when he was a student in Berlin. To solve the problem, we observe that, by the Reflection Principle, the two angles formed by each pair of sides of the minimal inscribed triangle with the corresponding tangent side of the given triangle must be equal. In other words, the vertices of the minimal inscribed triangle (or triangles) are the only points on the sides of the given triangle to which a billiard ball would return after exactly two reflections. The beauty of Fejér's argument is that it tells in a simple way how to locate the vertices of the minimal triangle.

Suppose that the given triangle is ABC. One way of trying to find the inscribed triangle UVW of minimum perimeter would be (a) to

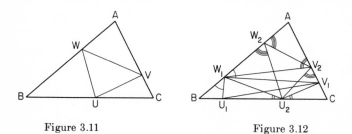

Figure 3.11   Figure 3.12

pick any points U_1 and V_1 on the sides BC and AC, respectively, and to choose W_1 on side AB so that the sum $\overline{U_1W_1} + \overline{V_1W_1}$ is as small as possible (see Fig. 3.12); (b) to keep V_1 and W_1 fixed and to determine that point U_2 on BC which minimizes the sum $\overline{W_1U_2} + \overline{V_1U_2}$; (c) to keep W_1 and U_2 fixed and to determine V_2 on AC so that $\overline{U_2V_2} + \overline{W_1V_2}$ is minimized; and (d) with U_2 and V_2 fixed, to find W_2 so as to minimize $\overline{U_2W_2} + \overline{V_2W_2}$; and so forth. This process would not stop in a finite number of steps except in special cases. Moreover, one would have to prove that this infinite process leads to a limiting triangle UVW.

Fejér avoided this difficulty. His idea was to fix U and to find the best possible position for V and W—the position such that the perimeter of $\triangle UVW$ is smallest—in one bright stroke. To do this, he reflected U in the two sides AB and AC, thinking of them as mirrors. (See Fig. 3.13.) Let us call the mirror images U' and U''. Then

$$\overline{U'W} + \overline{WV} + \overline{VU''} = \overline{UW} + \overline{WV} + \overline{VU}.$$

But the first sum is smallest when V and W lie on the straight line determined by U' and U''. Thus, given U, we have determined the position of V and W which minimizes the perimeter of $\triangle UVW$.

We now need only to find the best position for U. (See Fig. 3.14.) Since AB and AC are the perpendicular bisectors of UU' and UU'', respectively, $\triangle U'AU''$ is isosceles with $\overline{AU'} = \overline{AU} = \overline{AU''}$. The base $U'U''$ of $\triangle U'AU''$ has for its length the perimeter of $\triangle UVW$. Since $\measuredangle U'AU'' = 2 \measuredangle BAC$, the angle $U'AU''$ is fixed. Therefore, the base of $\triangle U'AU''$ will be shortest when its equal legs are shortest. The legs are shortest when AU is shortest, and the smallest possible value for $\overline{AU}$ occurs when AU is perpendicular to BC, that is, when AU is an altitude. The fact that $\triangle ABC$ is acute-angled guarantees that the foot of the altitude from A does lie on the side BC. Thus, we have now uniquely specified the inscribed triangle of least perimeter.

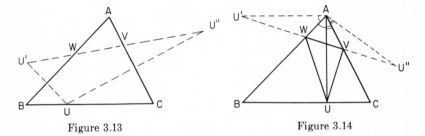

Figure 3.13   Figure 3.14

Moreover, it is clear that if $\triangle UVW$ is minimal, whatever property U has with respect to A, V has the same property with respect to B, and W has it with respect to C. This is true, since in the beginning we could have fixed either V or W instead of U. Consequently, we have proved

THEOREM 17. *Given an acute-angled triangle, the vertices of the inscribed triangle with the smallest perimeter are the feet of the altitudes of the given triangle.*

This minimal triangle is called the *pedal* triangle. Theorem 17 deals indirectly with the problem of hitting a ball on a triangular billiard table so that it will return to its original position after two reflections. The theorem shows that we can do this for particular positions of the ball. Before you investigate whether or not it can be done from any position try to solve:

PROBLEM 30. In what directions can one hit a ball lying on a rectangular billiard table so that it will return to its original position after a finite number of reflections? In what directions can one hit a ball so that it will strike another ball on the table? Can you solve these problems for billiard tables of any other shape? Assume that the balls are points.

Hint. Reflect the table and the ball using the sides of the table as mirrors; then reflect the reflections; etc.

PROBLEM 31. What property must the n-gon of least perimeter inscribed in a convex n-gon have if it exists?

A conjecture which was first made just a few years ago and which is related to the problem we have just solved is:

CONJECTURE. A triangle is inscribed in a given triangle dividing it into four smaller triangles. The perimeter of the inscribed triangle can never be smaller than the perimeters of each of the other three triangles.

As yet no one has found a proof for this conjectured theorem. The problem obtained by replacing the word "perimeter" in the above conjecture by "area" has been solved by a method not based on the ideas treated in this book.

In 1935 Paul Erdös conjectured a novel theorem concerning triangles.

THEOREM 18 (Erdös-Mordell). *If P is any point of a triangle ABC (inside or on the boundary) and if p_a, p_b, and p_c are the distances from P to the sides of $\triangle ABC$ [see Fig. 3.24(a) on page 86], then*

$$\overline{PA} + \overline{PB} + \overline{PC} \geq 2(p_a + p_b + p_c).$$

Further, equality holds above if and only if $\triangle ABC$ is equilateral and the point P is its circumcenter.

Two years later, in 1937, L. J. Mordell and D. R. Barrow proved Erdös' conjecture, but neither's proof was elementary. More recently, in 1945, D. K. Kazarinoff found an elementary proof which is based upon the idea of reflection. Before presenting his proof, we shall provide some motivation for Erdös' conjecture, and we shall prove some auxiliary theorems.

How was Erdös led to make his conjecture? What evidence did he have to suggest the idea? One possibility is that he generalized Euler's Inequality

$$R \geq 2r$$

between the circumradius R and the inradius r of a triangle, where equality holds only if the triangle is equilateral. This inequality is a consequence of a theorem proved by Euler.

THEOREM (Euler). *The square of the distance between the centers of the incircle and circumcircle of a triangle is $R^2 - 2Rr$.*

For, since

$$R^2 - 2Rr \geq 0 \quad \text{and} \quad R > 0,$$
$$R - 2r \geq 0.$$

The sum $\overline{PA} + \overline{PB} + \overline{PC}$ is analogous to $3R$, and the sum $p_a + p_b + p_c$ is analogous to $3r$; hence, it is reasonable to make the conjecture which Erdös did make. However, he probably had more evidence.

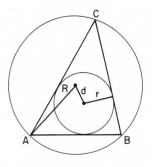

Figure 3.15

Since Euler's Inequality $R \geq 2r$ is an interesting result in itself, we shall interrupt our discussion of the Erdös-Mordell Inequality and first present two proofs of the inequality $R \geq 2r$. The first proof establishes Euler's Theorem that $d^2 = R^2 - 2Rr$, where d is the distance between the incenter and circumcenter of a triangle. The second proof establishes only the inequality $R \geq 2r$ and uses, at least implicitly, the idea of reflection.

In the course of the first proof, we shall use the following two lemmas.

LEMMA 1. *Let XY be a diameter of a circle with center at O (see Fig. 3.16). Let XY be intersected by a chord AE of this circle, and let O' be the point of intersection. Then*

$$\overline{AO'} \cdot \overline{O'E} = \overline{XO'} \cdot \overline{O'Y}.$$

PROOF. The triangles $O'AY$ and $O'XE$ are similar because

$$\sphericalangle AO'Y = \sphericalangle XO'E \quad \text{and} \quad \sphericalangle XEO' = \sphericalangle AYO'.$$

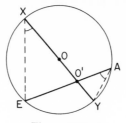

Figure 3.16

Therefore

$$\frac{\overline{AO'}}{\overline{XO'}} = \frac{\overline{O'Y}}{\overline{O'E}} \cdot \blacksquare$$

(If XY is not a diameter but any chord intersecting AE, the above proof and result remain valid.)

LEMMA 2. *Let ABC (see Fig. 3.17) be a triangle with incenter O', and let E be the midpoint of the arc BC (not containing A) of the circumcircle of ABC. Then*

$$\overline{EB} = \overline{EO'} = \overline{EC}.$$

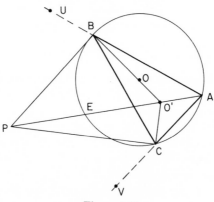

Figure 3.17

PROOF. Let P be the excenter of $\triangle ABC$ opposite A; that is, let P be the point of intersection of the bisectors of the angle A and the exterior angles UBC and VCB (see Fig. 3.17). (It is easy to show that these three lines meet in one point.) The bisectors BO' and BP are perpendicular since the angles they bisect make a straight angle;

similarly, the bisectors CO' and CP are perpendicular. Therefore, O' and P are endpoints of a diameter of a circle which passes through B and C. The center of this circle is the point of intersection of its diameter $O'P$ with the perpendicular bisector of one of its chords, BC. But $AO'P$ is the bisector of $\angle BAC$. Therefore, $AO'P$ cuts the arc BC (not containing A) of the circumcircle of $\triangle ABC$ at its midpoint. This midpoint is also a point of the perpendicular bisector of BC. Consequently, the midpoint E is the center of the circle through P, C, O', and B, and $\overline{EB} = \overline{EO'} = \overline{EC}.$ ∎

PROOF OF EULER'S THEOREM.† Let ABC be the given triangle, let O and O' be its circumcenter and incenter respectively, let D lie on AB with $O'D$ perpendicular to AB, let E be the point bisecting the arc BC (the one which does not contain A), and let EOF and $XOO'Y$ be diameters of the circumcircle. Denoting $\overline{OO'}$ by d, we have

$$\overline{XO'} = R + d \quad \text{and} \quad \overline{O'Y} = R - d.$$

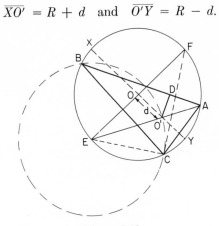

Figure 3.18

By Lemma 1,

$$\overline{AO'} \cdot \overline{O'E} = (R - d)(R + d).$$

By Lemma 2,

$$\overline{O'E} = \overline{EC}.$$

Thus

$$(R - d)(R + d) = \overline{AO'} \cdot \overline{EC}.$$

† Another proof is contained in the *Hungarian Problem Book* (to appear in this series); see Note 2 to problem 1897/2. That proof is due to L. Fejér, who was then a high school student.

The triangles $AO'D$ and FEC are right triangles. But the angles DAO' (that is, BAE) and CFE are equal since they cut off equal arcs ($\overset{\frown}{BE}$ and $\overset{\frown}{EC}$) from the circumcircle. Therefore, triangles $AO'D$ and FEC are similar. Consequently,

$$\frac{\overline{AO'}}{\overline{EF}} = \frac{\overline{O'D}}{\overline{EC}} \qquad \text{or} \qquad \overline{O'D}\cdot\overline{EF} = \overline{AO'}\cdot\overline{EC}.$$

Since $\overline{O'D} = r$ and $\overline{EF} = 2R$, this equality may be written as

$$r\cdot 2R = (R - d)(R + d) = R^2 - d^2.$$

Hence,

$$d^2 = R^2 - 2Rr\cdot \ \blacksquare$$

We have already shown that, since $R > 0$, the last equality implies the inequality $R \geq 2r$.

In the course of the second proof of the inequality $R \geq 2r$, we shall also need two lemmas.

LEMMA 3. Consider a triangle with a fixed base BC whose vertex V lies on a line l parallel to BC (see Fig. 3.19). Let MQ be the perpendicular bisector of BC. Then, as V moves closer to Q along l, the inradius of triangle VBC increases.

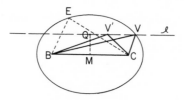

Figure 3.19

PROOF. Construct the ellipse with foci at B and C such that every point E on the ellipse satisfies the condition

$$\overline{BE} + \overline{EC} = \overline{BV} + \overline{VC}.$$

Then for any point V' on l for which $\overline{V'} < \overline{VQ}$,

$$\overline{BV'} + \overline{V'C} < \overline{BV} + \overline{VC}.$$

Since V' lies insides the ellipse, the perimeter P of triangle BVC is greater than the perimeter P' of triangle $BV'C$.

Let r be the inradius of triangle BVC, and let r' be that of triangle $BV'C$. Since the areas of these triangles are the same, we have (see solution of Problem 12)

$$T(BVC) = \frac{Pr}{2} = T(BV'C) = \frac{P'r'}{2}.$$

Since $P > P'$, it follows that $r < r'$. ∎

LEMMA 4. Consider a triangle with fixed base BC whose vertex U lies on a line l that makes a fixed angle with BC at C (see Fig. 3.20). As U moves away from C along l, the inradius of triangle UBC increases.

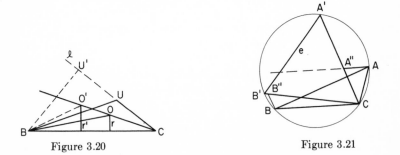

Figure 3.20   Figure 3.21

PROOF. Let $\overline{UC} < \overline{U'C}$. To compare the radii r and r' of the incircles of triangles UBC and $U'BC$, recall that the center of the incircle of a triangle is the point of intersection of its three angle bisectors. Clearly, as U moves along l away from C towards U', the angle at B increases and the point of intersection O of the angle bisectors moves away from C toward O' along the fixed angle bisector of $\angle\ C$. Therefore $r < r'$. ∎

SECOND PROOF OF THE INEQUALITY $R \geq 2r$. If the given triangle is equilateral, then $R = 2r$ and the equality is satisfied.

Suppose the given triangle is not equilateral. Label its vertices A, B, C, so that AC is its shortest side and so that the angle at A is smaller than the angle at C (see Fig. 3.21). Let R be the radius of the circumcircle K of triangle ABC, and let e be the side length of an equilateral triangle inscribed in K. Then $\overline{AC} < e$. From A, we move along the circumference of K, away from C, until we come to a point A' at which $\overline{A'C} = e$. Let B' be the third vertex of the equilateral triangle $A'B'C$. Denoting the inradius of a triangle XYZ by $r(XYZ)$, we shall now prove that

$$r(ABC) < r(A'BC) < r(A'B'C) = \frac{R}{2}$$

To prove the first inequality, we move A along a line parallel to BC until we come to A'' on $A'C$. By Lemma 1, $r(ABC) < r(A''BC)$. We then move from A'' to A' along $A'C$. By Lemma 2, $r(A''BC) < r(A'BC)$. Now the first inequality is established. To prove the second one, we move B to B'' along a line parallel to $A'C$ and then move from B'' to B' along $B'C$. Hence, if $\triangle ABC$ is not equilateral, $r(ABC) < R/2$ or $R > 2r(ABC)$. ∎

PROBLEM 32. Use the Principle of Reflection and the result: *Of all n-gons with the same area, the regular n-gon has the smallest perimeter* (that is, the dual of the statement following Problem 21) to show that if P is interior to a triangle ABC of area T, then

$$\overline{PA} + \overline{PB} + \overline{PC} \geq 2\sqrt{\sqrt{3}T}.$$

PROBLEM 33. Show that the last inequality implies that

$$\overline{PA} + \overline{PB} + \overline{PC} \geq 6r = 2(r + r + r).$$

This result further supports Theorem 18. Draw a triangle, and choose an interior point P. Measure its distances to the vertices and sides. Does the result support the theorem?

In order to prove the Erdös-Mordell Theorem, D. K. Kazarinoff used a little known but beautiful generalization of the Pythagorean Theorem, a theorem due to Pappus.

THEOREM 19 (Pappus). *Let ABC be any triangle. Let $AA'C'C$ and $BB''C''C$ be any two parallelograms constructed on AC and BC so that either both parallelograms are outside the triangle or both are not entirely*

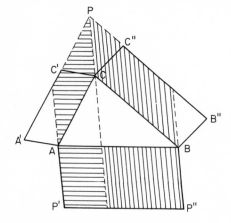

Figure 3.22

outside the triangle (see Fig. 3.22). *Prolong their sides $A'C'$ and $B''C''$ to meet in P. Construct a third parallelogram $ABP''P'$ on AB with AP' parallel to CP and with $\overline{AP'} = \overline{CP}$. The area of $\square$ $ABP''P'$ is equal to the sum of the areas of the parallelograms $AA'C'C$ and $BB''C''C$.*

The proof of this theorem, in case the parallelograms are outside the triangle, is contained in Fig. 3.22; the proof for the other case is just as simple. Note that when the given triangle is a right triangle and the given parallelograms are squares on its legs, then Pappus' Theorem specializes to the Pythagorean Theorem.

PROBLEM 34. Suppose that the parallelograms on the sides AC and BC of triangle ABC have a common edge. Generalize Pappus' Theorem to three-dimensional space in this case.

Note that the case considered in Problem 34 is actually not a special case; the general case can always be reduced to it (see Fig. 3.22 in which PC is the common edge of the shaded parallelograms). In the proof of Theorem 18 below, we shall apply Pappus' Theorem in this apparently special case.

There is one more theorem from plane geometry which we shall use in the proof of Theorem 18. It tells us under what conditions the sign of equality holds in the inequality

$$\overline{PA} + \overline{PB} + \overline{PC} \geq 2(p_a + p_b + p_c).$$

LEMMA. *Given a triangle ABC with circumcenter O, the bisector of the angle at A also bisects the angle between AO and the altitude from A to side BC.*

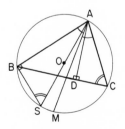

Figure 3.23

PROOF. Let AD be the altitude, AM the bisector of $\angle A$, and AOS a diameter of the circumcircle (see Fig. 3.23). Then $\angle ABS$ and $\angle ADC$ are right angles; moreover, $\angle ASB = \angle ACD$ because both angles are measured by $\frac{1}{2}\widehat{AB}$. Therefore, triangles CAD and SAB are similar, and $\angle BAS = \angle DAC$. Since AM is the bisector of $\angle A$,

$$\angle SAM = \angle DAM. \blacksquare$$

We can now prove the Erdös-Mordell Inequality—Theorem 18. The key to the proof is in the first step, which is an application of a reflection. Let triangle ABC be given, and let P be any point in its interior or on its boundary. [See Fig. 3.24(a).] We replace $\triangle ABC$ by a new triangle $AB'C'$, where B' and C' are the reflections of B and C, respectively, with respect to the bisector AD of the angle at A [see Fig. 3.24(b)]. We do not disturb the point P; this is important to remember. We apply Pappus' Theorem to $\triangle AB'C'$ considering the two given parallelograms to be those determined by A, P, and C' and A, P, and B' [see Figs. 3.24 (c) and (d)]. The sum of their areas is

$$cp_b + bp_c .$$

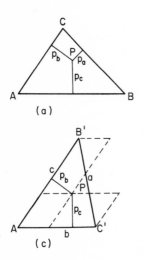

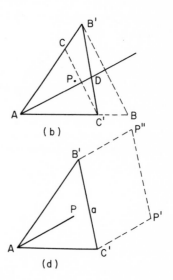

Figure 3.24

The area of the third parallelogram (the one having base $B'C'$ of length a and adjacent sides equal and parallel to PA) is less than or equal to $a \cdot \overline{PA}$, equality holding if and only if AP is perpendicular to $B'C'$. By the lemma stated on page 85, this occurs only if P lies on AO, where O is the circumcenter of $\triangle ABC$. Thus, by Pappus' Theorem,

$$cp_b + bp_c \leq a\overline{PA}$$

or

$$\frac{c}{a}p_b + \frac{b}{a}p_c \leq \overline{PA}.$$

Similarly,

$$\frac{a}{b}p_c + \frac{c}{b}p_a \leq \overline{PB}$$

and

$$\frac{b}{c}p_a + \frac{a}{c}p_b \leq \overline{PC}.$$

Adding the right- and left-hand sides, respectively, of the last three inequalities, we find that

$$\overline{PA} + \overline{PB} + \overline{PC} \geq \left(\frac{b}{c} + \frac{c}{b}\right)p_a + \left(\frac{c}{a} + \frac{a}{c}\right)p_b + \left(\frac{a}{b} + \frac{b}{a}\right)p_c.$$

Each of the coefficients on the right-hand side is at least 2. Why? (See Section 1.2 if you are puzzled.) Therefore

$$\overline{PA} + \overline{PB} + \overline{PC} \geq 2(p_a + p_b + p_c).$$

Equality holds if and only if $a = b = c$ and P lies on AO, BO, and CO; that is, equality holds if and only if $\triangle ABC$ is equilateral and P is its center. ∎

A second elementary proof of the Erdös-Mordell Inequality has been found by L. Bankoff, *American Mathematical Monthly*, Volume 65 (1958), p. 521.

PROBLEM 35. If P lies in a triangle ABC, then

$$\overline{PA} \cdot \overline{PB} \cdot \overline{PC} \geq 8\, p_a \cdot p_b \cdot p_c.$$

Equality holds only if the triangle is equilateral and P is its center. *Hint.* Use the inequalities $a\overline{PA} \geq cp_b + bp_c$, etc., and Theorem 8.

The next two problems are due to Professor A. Oppenheim of the University of Malaya; he rates Problem 35B as a hard problem.

PROBLEM 35A. Let $q_a = p_b + p_c$, let $q_b = p_a + p_c$, and let

$$q_c = p_a + p_b.$$

Prove that

$$\overline{PA} \cdot \overline{PB} \cdot \overline{PC} \geq q_a q_b q_c.$$

PROBLEM 35B. Prove that

$$\overline{PB} \cdot \overline{PC} + \overline{PC} \cdot \overline{PA} + \overline{PA} \cdot \overline{PB} \geq q_b q_c + q_c q_a + q_a q_b.$$

PROBLEM 36. Find the generalization of the Erdös-Mordell Inequality for triangles to three-dimensional space. We note that while the correct generalization is known, no one has discovered a proof. What are other possible inequalities which involve the distances from a point P inside a tetrahedron to the faces, edges, and vertices of the tetrahedron?

PROBLEM 37. In a given convex quadrilateral, which is the point such that the sum of its distances to the vertices is a minimum? What is the solution if the quadrilateral is not convex?

PROBLEM 38. What is the solution to the above problem for a triangle instead of a quadrilateral? Consider an acute-angled triangle first.

Miscellaneous Problems

PROBLEM 39. Find the largest rhombus inside a given triangle, one of whose angles is an angle of the triangle; see Fig. 3.25.

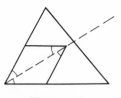

Figure 3.25

PROBLEM 40. Suppose the sides of a triangle ABC are in the relation $a < b < c$. If s_a, s_b, and s_c are the lengths of the medians from the vertices A, B, and C, respectively, and if f_a, f_b, and f_c are the lengths of the angle bisectors from these vertices, show that

$$s_a > s_b > s_c \quad \text{and} \quad f_a > f_b > f_c .$$

PROBLEM 41 (Erdös). Let P be any point inside a triangle ABC, and suppose that AP, BP, and CP extended meet the sides at A', B', and C', respectively. Prove that $\overline{PA'} + \overline{PB'} + \overline{PC'}$ is less than the length of the longest side of the triangle.

PROBLEM 42. a, b, c, and d are positive. Show that

(a) $\qquad \dfrac{a}{b} < \dfrac{c}{d}$ implies that $\dfrac{a}{b} < \dfrac{a+c}{b+d} < \dfrac{c}{d}$.

(b) $\qquad \dfrac{a}{\sqrt{b}} + \dfrac{b}{\sqrt{a}} \geq \sqrt{a} + \sqrt{b}$.

(c) $\qquad \sqrt{a+b} \leq \sqrt{a} + \sqrt{b}$.

(d) $\qquad \left(1 + \dfrac{1}{6a}\right)^{-a} > \dfrac{5}{6}$ for $a = 1, 2, 3, \cdots$.

PROBLEM 43. Of all triangles cut off from a fixed angle C by straight lines passing through a fixed point H in the interior of the angle (see Fig. 3.26), which has the least area?

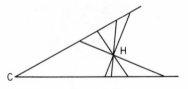

Figure 3.26

PROBLEM 44. Let the region $ABDC$ (see Fig. 3.27) be convex, and suppose AB is parallel to CD. What must be the position of a tangent EF to BD so that the area of $AEFC$ is a minimum? *Note.* A straight-line segment EF is *tangent* to the curve BD if EF and BD have at least one point in common and if all points of BD which are not on EF lie on the same side of EF.

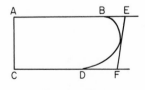

Figure 3.27

PROBLEM 45 (Fejes-Toth). On the surface of a sphere the distance between two points is the length of the shorter arc of a great circle having these two points as endpoints. Consider n points on the surface of a sphere, and let S be the sum of the distances between all distinct pairs of these points. One can ask: What positions of the n points yield the maximum value S_n of S? The question has been resolved in the cases $n = 2, 3, 4, 5$, and 6. Give the solution for $n \leq 4$. Can you conjecture what the values of S_{2k} and S_{2k+1} are? Can you give an inequality for S_n?

PROBLEM 46. Which is the shortest area-bisecting chord of a triangle? Which is the longest?
Hint. First, prove the following theorem.

THEOREM. *Of two triangles which have a common angle and area, the one with the smaller difference between the lengths of the sides forming that angle has the smaller base.*

PROBLEM 47. Replace "area" by "perimeter" in Problem 46 and solve the new problems.

PROBLEM 48. Let Q be a convex quadrilateral with perimeter P. Suppose that l and m are two perpendicular chords which divide the perimeter of Q into four equal parts. Show that if L is the sum of the lengths of m and l, then $L \geq P/2$ with equality holding only for rectangles. This problem is unsolved except in special cases.

CHAPTER FOUR

Hints and Solutions

The best advice I can offer on how to solve problems and prove theorems is: solve problems and prove theorems; concoct examples for evidence and hints as to general statements; consider special cases; make guesses and decide if your examples support or invalidate them; try to use, or modify and then use, reasoning you have employed or encountered in other situations; if you become stymied, rest and renew your efforts another day; use pencil and paper; keep a record of your thoughts. The more curious you become, the more experience you will acquire and the more you will learn. Think about mathematics, do mathematics, enjoy mathematics!

For a careful development and illustrations of the above suggestions and many more, I recommend that you read G. Pólya's books, *How to Solve It*, Princeton University Press, 1945 and *Mathematics and Plausible Reasoning* (especially Vol. I), Princeton University Press, 1954. When all else fails, then in good conscience you may read from the hints and solutions given below; but only read as much of a solution as you need to complete it by yourself.

It is good to remember that problems fall into three classes: can't, think I can, and have. When you *have* completed your solution—this means you have it written down so that someone who does not yet

91

know the solution and who is also fussy and critical can read it and understand it without having to fill in details you have neglected to describe—then compare the argument in the text with yours. Once you see how a problem is solved or a theorem is proved, attempt to provide a different solution or proof. Can you improve either the solution you have found or the one I have given? Incidentally, if you solve one of the unsolved problems mentioned in this pamphlet, send your solution to the editors of the NML series or to me.

Not all the problems and exercises given in the text are discussed below. When a particular question is discussed, it may be that only a hint or part of a solution is given. Sometimes other problems and theorems are mentioned. Almost every solution needs further work. In writing each one down, I have assumed that the reader is familiar with the problem and has seriously attempted to solve it.

EXERCISE 1. Definition 1 reveals that

$$7 < 9;$$

and using Theorem 4 with $p = \frac{1}{2}$, we find that

$$\sqrt{7} < 3.$$

The desired conclusion now follows from Theorem 2. ∎

EXERCISE 4. $\sqrt{1/3} + \sqrt{2/7}$ is larger. We discover this as follows. If

$$\sqrt{\frac{5}{12}} + \sqrt{\frac{1}{5}} < \sqrt{\frac{1}{3}} + \sqrt{\frac{2}{7}},$$

then, by Theorem 4 with $p = 2$,

$$\frac{5}{12} + 2\sqrt{\frac{5}{60}} + \frac{1}{5} < \frac{1}{3} + 2\sqrt{\frac{2}{21}} + \frac{2}{7}$$

or

$$\frac{5}{12} + \sqrt{\frac{20}{60}} + \frac{1}{5} < \frac{1}{3} + \sqrt{\frac{8}{21}} + \frac{2}{7};$$

hence,

$$\sqrt{\frac{1}{3}} - \sqrt{\frac{8}{21}} < \frac{1}{3} + \frac{2}{7} - \frac{5}{12} - \frac{1}{5} = \frac{1}{5 \cdot 7 \cdot 12}.$$

But $8/21 > 1/3$. Therefore, the left-hand member of the above inequality is a negative number, and the inequality is indeed correct.

Write out a careful proof by reversing the order of the above steps and adding to them where necessary.

PROBLEM 1. We first prove that

$$(*) \qquad \frac{2k-1}{2k} > \frac{\sqrt{4k-3}}{\sqrt{4k+1}} \qquad (k = 1, 2, 3, \cdots, n).$$

By adding $16 \, k^3 - 12k^2$ to both sides of the obviously correct statement $1 > 0$, we obtain the inequality

$$16k^3 - 12k^2 + 1 > 16k^3 - 12k^2$$

or

$$(2k-1)^2(4k+1) > (2k)^2(4k-3),$$

which, by Theorems 3 and 4, is equivalent to $(*)$. (In practice, one begins by assuming that $(*)$ is true, deduces $1 > 0$, and then reverses the steps to obtain a proof.)

The statements of the inequality $(*)$ for each of the integers 1 through n are:

$$\frac{1}{2} > \frac{1}{\sqrt{5}}, \qquad \frac{3}{4} > \frac{\sqrt{5}}{3}, \qquad \cdots, \qquad \frac{2n-3}{2n-2} > \frac{\sqrt{4n-7}}{\sqrt{4n-3}},$$

$$\frac{2n-1}{2n} > \frac{\sqrt{4n-3}}{\sqrt{4n-1}}.$$

The product of all the left-hand members is

$$\frac{1}{2} \cdot \frac{3}{4} \cdot \frac{5}{6} \cdot \cdots \cdot \frac{2n-3}{2n-2} \cdot \frac{2n-1}{2n}.$$

The product of all the right-hand members is

$$\frac{1}{\sqrt{5}} \cdot \frac{\sqrt{5}}{3} \cdot \frac{3}{\sqrt{13}} \cdot \cdots \cdot \frac{\sqrt{4n-7}}{\sqrt{4n-3}} \cdot \frac{\sqrt{4n-3}}{\sqrt{4n-1}} = \frac{1}{\sqrt{4n+1}}.$$

Consequently, by Theorem 3,

$$\frac{1}{2} \cdot \frac{3}{4} \cdot \cdots \cdot \frac{2n-1}{2n} > \frac{1}{\sqrt{4n+1}}.$$

The second inequality in Problem 1 can be established by first proving that

$$\frac{2k-1}{2k} = \frac{\sqrt{3k-2}}{\sqrt{3k+1}} \qquad (k=1),$$

$$\frac{2k-1}{2k} < \frac{\sqrt{3k-2}}{\sqrt{3k+1}} \qquad (k=2,3,\cdots,n),$$

and then by proceeding in analogy with the preceding argument.

PROBLEM 2.

$$\frac{b_1}{b_2} + \frac{b_2}{b_3} + \frac{b_3}{b_4} + \cdots + \frac{b_{n-1}}{b_n} + \frac{b_n}{b_1} \geq n$$

$(b_i > 0, i = 1, 2, \cdots, n)$ is the desired inequality. Equality holds only if $b_1 = b_2 = \cdots = b_n$.
Note that

$$\left(\frac{b_1}{b_2}\right)\left(\frac{b_2}{b_3}\right)\cdots\left(\frac{b_n}{b_1}\right) = 1.$$

PROBLEM 3. It is a consequence of the definition of $\log_{10} a$ and $\log_a 10$ that

$$\log_{10} a = (\log_a 10)^{-1}.$$

To see this, let $\log_a 10 = N$. Then

$$a^N = 10 \quad \text{and} \quad a = 10^{1/N}$$

so that

$$\frac{1}{N} = \log_{10} a.$$

Now use Theorem 6. (If you need more details, observe that

$$\log_{10} a + \log_a 10 = \log_{10} a + \frac{1}{\log_{10} a},$$

let $\log_{10} a = x$, and use inequality (3) on page 18.) ∎

PROBLEM 4.

$$\sqrt[n+1]{ab^n} = \sqrt[n+1]{\underbrace{a \cdot b \cdot b \cdot \cdots \cdot b}_{n+1 \text{ factors}}} \leq \frac{\overbrace{a + b + \cdots + b}^{n+1 \text{ terms}}}{n+1} \quad \text{(Theorem 8)}$$

$$= \frac{a + nb}{n+1}.$$

Equality holds only if $a = b$. ∎

PROBLEM 5.

$$n! = 1 \cdot 2 \cdot 3 \cdot \cdots \cdot n < \left(\frac{1 + 2 + \cdots + n}{n}\right)^n \quad \text{(Theorem 8)}.$$

But

$$1 + 2 + 3 + \cdots + n$$

$$= \frac{1}{2}\left\{ \begin{matrix} 1 & + & 2 & + & 3 & + \cdots + n - 1 + & n \\ +n & + & n - 1 & + n - 2 + & \cdots + & 2 & + & 1 \end{matrix} \right\}$$

$$= \frac{1}{2}\left\{(n+1) + (n+1) + (n+1) + \cdots + (n+1) + (n+1)\right\}$$

$$= \frac{n(n+1)}{2}.$$

Therefore, by Theorem 1,

$$n! < \left[\frac{n(n+1)}{n \cdot 2}\right]^n = \left(\frac{n+1}{2}\right)^n,$$

which was to be shown. ∎

PROBLEM 6. If a, b, and c are positive,

$$ab + bc + ca \geq 3(ab \cdot bc \cdot ca)^{1/3} = 3(abc)^{2/3} \quad \text{(Theorem 8)};$$

and

$$a + b + c \geq 3(abc)^{1/3} \quad \text{(Theorem 8)}.$$

Therefore, by Theorem 3, if a, b, and c are positive,

$$(a + b + c)(ab + bc + ca) \geq 9abc.$$

If $a = b = c$, equality holds. If two or more of a, b, and c are zero, equality holds. In all other cases inequality holds.

PROBLEM 7, *Solution* 1. One can arrange the terms in the product as follows:

$$\left(\sum_1^n a_i\right)\left(\sum_1^n \frac{1}{a_i}\right) = \frac{a_1}{a_1} + \frac{a_2}{a_2} + \cdots \quad \cdots \quad \cdots \quad + \frac{a_n}{a_n}$$
$$+ \left(\frac{a_1}{a_2} + \frac{a_2}{a_1}\right) + \left(\frac{a_1}{a_3} + \frac{a_3}{a_1}\right) + \cdots + \left(\frac{a_1}{a_n} + \frac{a_n}{a_1}\right)$$
$$+ \left(\frac{a_2}{a_3} + \frac{a_3}{a_2}\right) + \cdots + \left(\frac{a_2}{a_n} + \frac{a_n}{a_2}\right)$$
$$\cdot \quad \cdot$$
$$+ \left(\frac{a_{n-1}}{a_n} + \frac{a_n}{a_{n-1}}\right).$$

Considering each row of terms separately and using inequality (3) on page 18, we conclude that each term in every row except the first is greater than 2, and hence that

$$\left(\sum_1^n a_i\right)\left(\sum_1^n \frac{1}{a_i}\right) \geq n\cdot 1 + (n-1)\cdot 2 + (n-2)\cdot 2 + \cdots$$
$$+ [n - (n-2)]\cdot 2 + 1\cdot 2;$$

or

$$\left(\sum_1^n a_i\right)\left(\sum_1^n \frac{1}{a_i}\right) \geq 2\left[\sum_{k=1}^n (n-k)\right] + n = 2\frac{n(n-1)}{2} + n = n^2.$$

Equality holds only if $a_1 = a_2 = \cdots = a_n$. ∎

Solution 2. Another way of arranging the terms is

$$\left(\sum_1^n a_i\right)\left(\sum_1^n \frac{1}{a_i}\right) = \frac{a_1}{a_1} + \frac{a_1}{a_2} + \frac{a_1}{a_3} + \cdots + \frac{a_1}{a_{n-1}} + \frac{a_1}{a_n}$$
$$+ \frac{a_2}{a_1} + \frac{a_2}{a_2} + \frac{a_2}{a_3} + \cdots + \frac{a_2}{a_{n-1}} + \frac{a_2}{a_n}$$
$$+ \frac{a_3}{a_1} + \frac{a_3}{a_2} + \frac{a_3}{a_3} + \cdots + \frac{a_3}{a_{n-1}} + \frac{a_3}{a_n}$$
$$\cdot \cdot \cdot \cdot \cdot$$
$$+ \frac{a_{n-1}}{a_1} + \frac{a_{n-1}}{a_2} + \frac{a_{n-1}}{a_3} + \cdots + \frac{a_{n-1}}{a_{n-1}} + \frac{a_{n-1}}{a_n}$$
$$+ \frac{a_n}{a_1} + \frac{a_n}{a_2} + \frac{a_n}{a_3} + \cdots + \frac{a_n}{a_{n-1}} + \frac{a_n}{a_n}.$$

There are exactly n^2 terms in this sum, n rows of n terms each. Observing the rows and columns, we see that exactly n terms have the numerator a_k for each k from 1 to n and that exactly n terms have the denominator a_k for each k from 1 to n. Therefore, the product of all these n^2 positive fractions is 1; hence, by Theorem 6, their sum is at least n^2. Equality holds if and only if they are all equal, that is, if and only if $a_1 = a_2 = \cdots = a_n$. ∎

Can you find still another solution—one involving the result of Problem 2 as applied to diagonal rows of terms in the sum of n^2 terms above?

PROBLEM 8. A line of discovery of a proof is given below. If

$$|a| - |b| \leq |a + b| \leq |a| + |b|,$$

then, by Theorem 4,

$$|a|^2 - 2|a| \cdot |b| + |b|^2 \leq |a + b|^2 \leq |a|^2 + 2|a| \cdot |b| + |b|^2$$

But $|a|^2 = a^2$, $|b|^2 = b^2$, and $|a + b|^2 = (a + b)^2$. Therefore, if we subtract a^2 and b^2 from all three members of the last inequality, we obtain the result

$$-2|a| \cdot |b| \leq 2ab \leq 2|a| \cdot |b|.$$

Since $|a| \geq a$ and since $|b| \geq b$, $|a| \cdot |b| \geq ab$. (Why?) Therefore, it *is* true that

$$-2|a| \cdot |b| \leq 2ab \leq 2|a| \cdot |b|.$$

In order to write down a proof, we must be able to reverse the order of the above steps. Such a reversal may not be possible. For example, if $x > y > 1$, $x^2 > y^2 > 1$; but if $x^2 > y^2 > 1$, it need not be that $x > y > 1$; suppose $x = -4$ and $y = -3$. However, in the case at hand, we *can* reverse our steps.

PROOF. Clearly, $|a|^2 = a^2$, $|b|^2 = b^2$, $|a| \cdot |b| \geq ab$, and $-|a| \cdot |b| \leq ab$. Therefore, by Theorem 2,

$$|a|^2 - 2|a| \cdot |b| + |b|^2 \leq a^2 + 2ab + b^2$$
$$\leq |a|^2 + 2|a| \cdot |b| + |b|^2.$$

Since $(a + b)^2 = |a + b|^2$, we obtain the desired conclusion from the last inequalities by using Theorem 4 with $p = \frac{1}{2}$. ∎

Note that the inequality $|a| - |b| \leq |a + b|$ actually implies that

$\| a | - | b \| \leq | a + b |$. (These inequalities are valid for *any* real numbers a and b.)

The number $| a + b |$ is the distance from the point a to the point $-b$ on the real line. The number $| a | + | b |$ is the distance from a to the origin plus the distance from $-b$ to the origin. Thus, the right-hand side of the inequality implies that the distance between two points on the real line (a and $-b$ may denote any pair of points depending on the values of a and b) is less than or equal to the sum of their distances to the origin. This geometric statement corresponds to the *triangle inequality*, namely, that the sum of the lengths of two sides of a triangle is greater than the length of the third side. Similarly, the left-hand inequality is equivalent to the theorem that the distance between two points on the real line is greater than or equal to the difference of their distances to the origin and corresponds to another well-known triangle inequality.

Can you prove and interpret the following inequalities?

(i) $| a | - | b | \leq | a - b | \leq | a | + | b |$.

(ii) $| a - c | - | b - c | \leq | a \pm b | \leq | a - c | + | b - c |$.

If a and b are complex numbers, then again

$$| a + b | \leq | a | + | b |,$$

and the geometric interpretation of this inequality for complex numbers is the triangle inequality cited above.

PROBLEM 9. Let $\triangle$ be a triangle with area T and perimeter P. Let $\triangle_1$ be an isosceles triangle with the same base and perimeter as $\triangle$ but with area T_1. Lastly, let $\triangle_2$ be an isosceles triangle with the same base and area as $\triangle$ but with perimeter P_2. By Theorem 10B as applied to $\triangle$ and $\triangle_2$,

$$P \geq P_2.$$

Thus, although $\triangle_1$ and $\triangle_2$ are both isosceles triangles with a common base, the perimeter of $\triangle_1$ is at least as great as the perimeter of $\triangle_2$. Consequently, the area of $\triangle_1$ is at least as great as the area of $\triangle_2$; that is, $T_1 \geq T$. ∎

Given the triangle $\triangle$, construct the triangles $\triangle_1$ and $\triangle_2$. See the truth of the theorem with your own eyes.

PROBLEM 10. I shall prove that Theorem 11A implies Theorem 11B. Let $\triangle$ be any triangle with area T and perimeter P. Let $\triangle_1$ be an equilateral triangle with area T and perimeter P_1. Lastly, let $\triangle_2$ be an equilateral triangle with area T_2 and perimeter P. By Theorem 11A as applied to $\triangle$ and $\triangle_2$,

$$T_2 \geq T.$$

Now, of two equilateral triangles, the one with the greater area has the greater perimeter (and, conversely, the one with the greater perimeter has the greater area). Thus, comparing $\triangle_1$ and $\triangle_2$, we conclude that $P_1 \leq P$. ∎

PROBLEM 11. Dividing both the left- and right-hand members in Heron's formula $(7')$ by $16T^2$, we have the result

$$\frac{P^{1/3}(P - 2a)}{(16T^2)^{1/3}} \cdot \frac{P^{1/3}(P - 2b)}{(16T^2)^{1/3}} \cdot \frac{P^{1/3}(P - 2c)}{(16T^2)^{1/3}} = 1.$$

Each factor in the above product is positive, so that we may apply Theorem 6 and conclude that the sum of the three numbers whose product is one is least when the three numbers are equal. The sum is

$$\left(\frac{P}{16T^2}\right)^{1/3}(P - 2a + P - 2b + P - 2c), \qquad \text{that is,} \qquad \frac{P^{4/3}}{(16T^2)^{1/3}}.$$

The three numbers are equal when $P - 2a = P - 2b = P - 2c$. This happens if and only if $a = b = c$. Since T is fixed, this means P is least when $a = b = c$. ∎

PROBLEM 12. The equilateral triangle is the extremal one in both cases.

Hint. Use the theorem that *of all triangles with the same perimeter (or area), the equilateral triangle has the largest inscribed circle.*

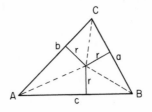

Figure 4.1

PROOF. For any triangle ABC,

$$2T = rP,$$

where r is the radius of its inscribed circle. This is true because

$$T = a \cdot \frac{r}{2} + b \cdot \frac{r}{2} + c \cdot \frac{r}{2} = (a + b + c)\frac{r}{2} = P \cdot \frac{r}{2}.$$

Theorem 11A states that for fixed P, T is greatest when ABC is equilateral. Hence for fixed P we see, from the relation $2T = rP$, that r is greatest when ABC is equilateral. A similar argument can be made if T is fixed. ∎

Solution to part of Problem 12. Let $\triangle$ be a triangle circumscribed about the given circle of radius r, and suppose $\triangle$ has perimeter P and area T. Let $\triangle_E$ be the equilateral triangle circumscribed about the same circle, and denote its area and perimeter by T_E and P_E, respectively. Lastly, let $\triangle_1$ be an equilateral triangle with perimeter P, and call the radius of its inscribed circle r_1. Applying the above theorem to $\triangle$ and $\triangle_1$, we conclude that $r_1 \geq r$. But if one equilateral triangle, $\triangle_1$, has a larger inscribed circle than another, $\triangle_E$, it also has a larger area and perimeter. Therefore $P \geq P_E$. ∎

PROBLEM 13. If one is going to present a long proof or use an argument with a large number of long steps, it is always a good policy to explain first what one is going to do. The solution of the present problem is just such an instance.   The answers to the two questions posed in Problem 13 are:

THEOREM A. *Of all triangles inscribed in a given circle, the equilateral triangle has the largest perimeter,*
and

THEOREM B. *Of all triangles inscribed in a given circle, the equilateral triangle has the largest area.*
We shall present a complete proof of the first of these two theorems, and we shall suggest how the second may be established. The proof of Theorem A has two main parts. We first prove

THEOREM C. *Of all triangles with the same base which are inscribed in a given circle, the isosceles triangle with the greater altitude has the greatest perimeter.*

We then prove that of all isosceles triangles inscribed in a given circle, the equilateral triangle has the greatest perimeter.

PROOF OF THEOREM C. Let ABC be the inscribed triangle with fixed vertices A and B. Let us denote the angles at A, B and C by α,

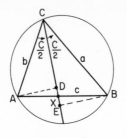

Figure 4.2

β and γ, respectively. As the vertex C moves along the circumference of the circle, the angle γ remains constant. Suppose the bisector of γ intersects the base AB at X. Let AD and BE be perpendiculars drawn to CX, perhaps extended (Fig. 4.2). Then

$$b \sin \tfrac{1}{2}\gamma = \overline{AD}, \qquad a \sin \tfrac{1}{2}\gamma = \overline{BE}$$

and

$(*) \qquad\qquad (a + b) \sin \tfrac{1}{2}\gamma = \overline{AD} + \overline{BE}.$

Also, in the case illustrated by Fig. 4.2,

$$\angle AXD = \beta + \tfrac{1}{2}\gamma,$$

so that

$$\angle XAD = \angle EBX = \tfrac{1}{2}\pi - (\beta + \tfrac{1}{2}\gamma)$$
$$= \tfrac{1}{2}(\alpha + \beta + \gamma) - (\beta + \tfrac{1}{2}\gamma)$$
$$= \tfrac{1}{2}(\alpha - \beta).$$

Therefore

$$\overline{AX} \cos \tfrac{1}{2}(\alpha - \beta) = \overline{AD}, \qquad \overline{BX} \cos \tfrac{1}{2}(\alpha - \beta) = \overline{BE},$$

and

$(**) \quad (\overline{AX} + \overline{BX}) \cos \tfrac{1}{2}(\alpha - \beta) = c \cos \tfrac{1}{2}(\alpha - \beta) = \overline{AD} + \overline{BE}.$

It is a consequence of $(*)$ and $(**)$ that

$$(a + b) \sin \tfrac{1}{2}\gamma = \overline{AD} + \overline{BE} = c \cos \tfrac{1}{2}(\alpha - \beta),$$

or

$$(a + b) = \frac{c \cos \tfrac{1}{2}(\alpha - \beta)}{\sin \tfrac{1}{2}\gamma}.$$

The angle γ is fixed, and $\cos \frac{1}{2}(\alpha - \beta)$ is greatest when $\alpha = \beta$, that is, when $\triangle ABC$ is isosceles. Therefore $a + b$ is greatest when $\triangle ABC$ is isosceles. Unless $\gamma = 90°$, there are two possible values for γ, according as C lies on one side of AB or the other. The smaller value corresponds to the larger value of $a + b$ among the two possible isosceles triangles ABC for fixed A and B; it also corresponds to the longer altitude from C to AB. ∎

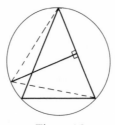

Figure 4.3

It is easy to show, with the help of this theorem, that an isosceles nonequilateral triangle inscribed in a given circle is not the triangle of maximum perimeter inscribable in that circle; we merely take one of the equal sides of the triangle as the new base and inscribe an isosceles triangle on this base (see Fig. 4.3). According to the theorem, the new triangle has a larger perimeter than the given one. Since we have not shown that, in a given circle, a triangle of maximum perimeter exists, the above method of increasing the perimeter of a nonequilateral triangle does not constitute a proof of the existence of the maximal figure. We therefore need to approach Theorem A from a different point of view.

PROOF OF THEOREM A. In view of Theorem C all we need to show is that, among all isosceles triangles inscribed in the given circle, the equilateral triangle has the greatest perimeter. Let $\triangle ABC$ be isosceles (see Fig. 4.4), let CC' be the diameter perpendicular to AB, and let AO be a radius of the given circle with $\overline{AO} = R$. We shall first show that the perimeter $2a + c$ is greatest when $\overline{AC'} = R$. Since, in this case, $\triangle ABC$ must be equilateral, the proof of the theorem will then be complete.

By the Pythagorean Theorem,

$$a = \sqrt{4R^2 - \overline{AC'}^2} \quad \text{and} \quad \frac{c}{2} = \sqrt{\overline{AC'}^2 - \overline{C'X}^2}.$$

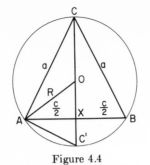

Figure 4.4

Since the triangles $AC'C$ and $AC'X$ are similar,

$$\frac{\overline{C'X}}{\overline{AC'}} = \frac{\overline{AC'}}{2R} \quad \text{or} \quad \overline{C'X} = \frac{\overline{AC'}^2}{2R}.$$

Consequently,

$$\frac{c}{2} = \sqrt{\overline{AC'}^2 - \left(\frac{\overline{AC'}^2}{2R}\right)^2} = \frac{\overline{AC'}}{2R}\sqrt{4R^2 - \overline{AC'}^2}$$

and

$$a + \frac{c}{2} = \sqrt{4R^2 - \overline{AC'}^2}\left(1 + \frac{\overline{AC'}}{2R}\right)$$

$$= \frac{1}{2R}\sqrt{2R + \overline{AC'}}\sqrt{2R - \overline{AC'}}\,(2R + \overline{AC'}).$$

We wish to find conditions under which $P = 2(a + c/2)$ is a maximum. Since R is fixed, P will be a maximum when $6R^2P^2$ is a maximum. We first observe that

$$6R^2P^2 = 12R^2\left(a + \frac{c}{2}\right)^2$$

$$= (2R + \overline{AC'})(2R + \overline{AC'})(2R + \overline{AC'})(6R - 3\overline{AC'}).$$

Secondly, we observe that $2R > \overline{AC'}$ and that the sum of the four factors on the right is $12R$, which does not depend on $\overline{AC'}$. We are thus able to use Theorem 7, which says that the product of four positive numbers with a given sum is greatest when they are all equal. The value of $\overline{AC'}$ which makes all factors equal is determined by the equality

$$6R - 3\overline{AC'} = 2R + \overline{AC'};$$

the result is

$$\overline{AC'} = R.$$

Therefore, $c = a$, and $\triangle ABC$ is equilateral. ∎

The method by which the equivalence of Theorems 10A and 10B was demonstrated can now be used to prove Theorem B:

Of all triangles inscribed in a given circle, the equilateral triangle has the greatest area.

However, this method cannot be used to prove that Theorem B implies Theorem A.

Theorem B is equivalent to the following proposition.

THEOREM. *The product of the lengths of the sides of an equilateral triangle inscribed in a circle is greater than the product of the lengths of the sides of any other triangle inscribed in the same circle.*

PROOF. For any triangle ABC (see Fig. 4.5),

$$T = \frac{ab \sin C}{2} \quad \text{and} \quad \sin C = \frac{c}{2R}; \quad \text{that is,} \quad T = \frac{abc}{4R}.$$

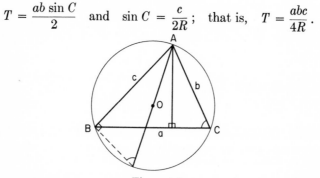

Figure 4.5

Since R is fixed, we conclude that T is greatest when $a \cdot b \cdot c$ is greatest, namely, when $a = b = c$. ∎

The preceding discussion illustrates a common phenomenon in mathematics: simple questions which require much labor to be answered.

PROBLEM 14. *Theorem. Of all triangles with a given perimeter, the equilateral triangle has the smallest circumcircle.*

PROOF. Let $\triangle$ be a triangle with circumradius R and perimeter P. Let $\triangle_E$ be an equilateral triangle with circumradius R and perimeter P_E. Lastly, let $\triangle'$ be an equilateral triangle with circumradius R' and perimeter P. By the result of Problem 13, $P_E \geq P$. Therefore

$$R \geq R'. \quad ∎$$

The theorem involving area instead of perimeter is similarly stated and proved. One simply replaces *perimeter* by *area* wherever it appears in the last theorem and proof.

PROBLEM 15. Let the dimensions of such a box be a, b, and c, with the open end having edges of lengths a and b; and denote its surface area and volume by S and V, respectively. Then

$$S = 2ac + 2bc + ab \quad \text{and} \quad V = abc.$$

By Theorem 8,

$$[(2ac)(2bc)(ab)]^{1/3} \leq \frac{S}{3}.$$

Since $(abc)^{2/3} = V^{2/3}$, this inequality is equivalent to

$$V^{2/3} \leq \frac{S}{3 \cdot 2^{2/3}} \quad \text{or} \quad V \leq \frac{S^{3/2}}{2 \cdot 3^{3/2}}.$$

The maximum value, $S^{3/2}/(2 \cdot 3^{3/2})$, of V is taken on if and only if

$$2ac = 2bc = ab,$$

that is, if and only if

$$a = b = 2c.$$

The box of maximum volume is therefore one half of a cube. ∎ Can you solve this problem using the Reflection Principle discussed in Chapter 3?

PROBLEM 16. Let the dimensions and volume of such a box be denoted as in the solution to Problem 15. Then $2b + 2c$ is the girth, and

$$a + 2b + 2c \leq L.$$

By Theorem 8,

$$(a \cdot 2b \cdot 2c)^{1/3} \leq \frac{a + 2b + 2c}{3} \leq \frac{L}{3} \quad \text{or} \quad 2^{2/3} \cdot V^{1/3} \leq \frac{L}{3}.$$

Therefore

$$V \leq \frac{L^3}{2^2 \cdot 3^3}.$$

When V is at its maximum, which is $L^3/(3^3 \cdot 2^2)$, then

$$a = 2b = 2c.$$

The height b and width c of the box should therefore be equal, and its length a should be twice its width (or twice its height).

PROBLEM 17. Let the dimensions of such a box be a, b, and c. Then the sum L of the lengths of its edges is $4(a + b + c)$. By Theorem 8,

$$(abc)^{1/3} \leq \frac{a + b + c}{3} \quad \text{or} \quad V^{1/3} \leq \frac{L}{12}.$$

Therefore, the volume is greatest when $V = (L/12)^3$, and this happens if and only if $a = b = c$.

The surface area S of the box is

$$2(ab + bc + ca).$$

By Theorem 8, $2ab \leq a^2 + b^2$, $2bc \leq b^2 + c^2$, and $2ca \leq c^2 + a^2$. Equality holds in all three inequalities if and only if $a = b = c$. Therefore,

$$S \leq 2(a^2 + b^2 + c^2) = 2(a + b + c)^2 - 4(ab + bc + ca)$$
$$= 2(a + b + c)^2 - 2S$$

or

$$3S \leq 2 \left(\frac{L}{4} \right)^2.$$

L is fixed. Hence S is a maximum when $a = b = c$. ▮

PROBLEM 18. *Hint.* Let M be a tetrahedron with volume V. If each face of M is an equilateral triangle, then M is a regular tetrahedron, and there is nothing to prove. Otherwise, choose a face which is not an equilateral triangle. Keeping the volume of M fixed, transform M by changing this face into an equilateral triangle of the same area and by moving the opposite vertex until it lies above the center of this triangle. This diminishes the surface area. Why? Can you prove it? Therefore, if M is not a regular tetrahedron with volume V, there is another tetrahedron with the same volume but with less surface area. By hypothesis, a solution to the problem exists. Therefore, the regular tetrahedron must be that solution.

In 1884, R. Sturm gave a proof of this theorem which was in the spirit of Steiner's proof of the isoperimetric theorem for triangles. He did not assume that an extremal tetrahedron exists. Although it is elementary, his proof is not simple.

Solution. We first observe that the inequality

$$(x^2 + u^2)^{1/2} + (y^2 + v^2)^{1/2} \geq [(x + y)^2 + (u + v)^2]^{1/2}$$

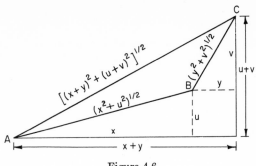

Figure 4.6

is valid for any positive numbers x, y, u, and v; this inequality is, according to Fig. 4.6, equivalent to $\overline{AB} + \overline{BC} \geq \overline{AC}$. Similarly, the inequality

$$(x^2 + u^2)^{1/2} + (y^2 + v^2)^{1/2} + (z^2 + w^2)^{1/2}$$
$$\geq [(x + y + z)^2 + (u + v + w)^2]^{1/2}$$

is equivalent to the statement $\overline{AB} + \overline{BC} + \overline{CD} \geq \overline{AD}$, where $ABCD$ is a polygonal path. We shall make use of this inequality in a moment. The above inequalities and their generalizations to sums of n terms were discovered and proved by the great geometer Hermann Minkowski (1864–1909).

Suppose the given tetrahedron M has volume V and total surface area S. If M is not regular, then at least one face is not equilateral, and we may assume it to be the base. We denote the base perimeter by P, and we denote the base area by A. Now suppose that N is the transformed tetrahedron with equilateral base and the same altitude. Then N has volume V, total surface area S^*, base perimeter $P^* < P$, and base area A.

Let h be the common altitude of M and N (see Fig. 4.7), let a, b, and c be the lengths of the sides of the base of M, and let e be the length of the sides of the base of N. Let p_a, p_b, and p_c be the lengths of the perpendiculars to the sides from the foot of the altitude of M to the base, and let p be the length of the corresponding perpendiculars for N. Then, considering M, we see that

$$A = \tfrac{1}{2}(ap_a + bp_b + cp_c),$$
$$S = A + \tfrac{1}{2}[a(p_a^2 + h^2)^{1/2} + b(p_b^2 + h^2)^{1/2} + c(p_c^2 + h^2)^{1/2}]$$

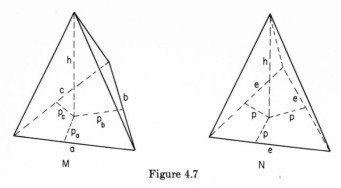

Figure 4.7

and

$$2(S - A) = (a^2 p_a^2 + a^2 h^2)^{1/2} + (b^2 p_b^2 + b^2 h^2)^{1/2} + (c^2 p_c^2 + c^2 h^2)^{1/2}.$$

Similarly, by considering N, we see that

$$A = \tfrac{1}{2}(ep + ep + ep) = \tfrac{1}{2}(3e)p = \tfrac{1}{2}P^*p,$$

$$S^* = A + \tfrac{1}{2}[e(p^2 + h^2)^{1/2} + e(p^2 + h^2)^{1/2} + e(p^2 + h^2)^{1/2}]$$

$$= A + \tfrac{1}{2}P^*(p^2 + h^2)^{1/2}$$

and

$$2(S^* - A) = (P^{*2}p^2 + P^{*2}h^2)^{1/2} = [(2A)^2 + P^{*2}h^2]^{1/2}.$$

We now set

$$ap_a = x, \qquad bp_b = y, \qquad cp_c = z; \qquad ah = u, \qquad bh = v, \qquad ch = w,$$

and we apply the second inequality stated at the beginning of this solution. Thus,

$$2(S - A) = (a^2 p_a^2 + a^2 h^2)^{1/2} + (b^2 p_b^2 + b^2 h^2)^{1/2} + (c^2 p_c^2 + c^2 h^2)^{1/2}$$

$$= (x^2 + u^2)^{1/2} + (y^2 + v^2)^{1/2} + (z^2 + w^2)^{1/2}$$

$$\geq [(x + y + z)^2 + (u + v + w)^2]^{1/2}$$

$$= [(ap_a + bp_b + cp_c)^2 + (ah + bh + ch)^2]^{1/2}$$

$$= [(2A)^2 + P^2 h^2]^{1/2}$$

$$> [(2A)^2 + P^{*2}h^2]^{1/2}$$

$$= 2(S^* - A).$$

But if $2(S - A) > 2(S^* - A)$, it follows that $S > S^*$. ∎

PROBLEM 19. Let such a double pyramid have volume V and surface area S. Let the constituent pyramids have bases of area a^2 and altitudes of length h. Then,

$$V = \frac{2a^2h}{3}, \qquad S = 4a\left[\left(\frac{a}{2}\right)^2 + h^2\right]^{1/2}, \qquad \text{and} \qquad S^2 = 4a^2(a^2 + 4h^2).$$

Hint. Write S^2 as $4[a^4 + 2a^2h^2 + 2a^2h^2]$, and minimize the sum in brackets using Theorem 8 for the case $n = 3$.

To extend the theorem to an oblique double pyramid Q with a square base, first transform Q into a right double pyramid R with the same base and with the same volume. If, for one of the oblique pyramids constituting Q, the distances from the foot of the altitude h to the base to the sides of the base are x_1, x_2, x_3, and x_4, then the lateral surface area S of Q is

$$2 \sum_{i=1}^{4} \tfrac{1}{2}a[x_i^2 + h^2]^{1/2}.$$

Therefore

$$S = a \sum_{i=1}^{4} [x_i^2 + h^2]^{1/2}$$

$$\geq a\left[\left(\sum_{i=1}^{4} x_i\right)^2 + \left(\sum_{i=1}^{4} h\right)^2\right]^{1/2} \qquad \text{(Why?)}$$

$$= a[(2a)^2 + (4h)^2]^{1/2}$$

$$= 4a\left[\left(\frac{a}{2}\right)^2 + h^2\right]^{1/2},$$

which is the surface area of R.

PROBLEM 20. Following the hint, we first observe that

$$A = n\left(r \cdot \frac{P}{2n}\right) = \frac{rP}{2}.$$

Therefore,

$$A^2 = \frac{r^2P^2}{4} \quad \text{and} \quad A = \frac{r^2P^2}{4A}.$$

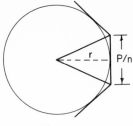

Figure 4.8

But $A > \pi r^2$, the area of the inscribed circle. Consequently, after replacing the A in the denominator of the last fraction by πr^2, we have the inequality

$$A < \frac{r^2 P^2}{4\pi r^2} = \frac{P^2}{4\pi}.$$

The radius of a circle with perimeter P is $P/2\pi$; hence its area is $\pi(P/2\pi)^2$ or $P^2/4\pi$. Thus we have shown that a circle of perimeter P has a greater area than a regular n-gon with perimeter P. ∎

PROBLEM 21. Let the n sides of the n-gon which can be inscribed in a circle be rigidly attached to the portions of the circle exterior to the n-gon, thus forming n movable pieces (see Fig. 4.9). Suppose their total area is K. If these pieces are arranged so as to bound any other n-gon with the same sides, then the new figure has the same perimeter as the circle (or less if the pieces overlap). Let T be the area of the new n-gon. By the Isoperimetric Theorem, the total area $T + K$ of the new figure (including overlapping) is less than the area $A + K$ of the circle. Therefore, $T < A$. ∎

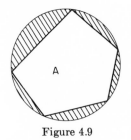

Figure 4.9

PROBLEM 23. *Hint.* The figures depicted in Fig. 4.10 each have the same total perimeter $L + L'$. Which has the greater area? Why?

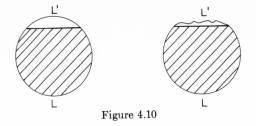

Figure 4.10

PROBLEM 24. *Hint.* The two *n*-gons with labeled sides which are depicted in Fig. 4.11 have $n-1$ corresponding sides equal and have the same perimeter.

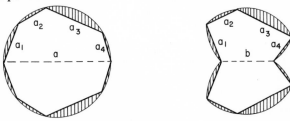

Figure 4.11

PROBLEM 25. *Hint.* The method implicit in Fig. 4.12 works only if the angle of the given sector of the plane is of the special form π/n, $n = 2, 3, \cdots$. In other cases, it is difficult to give a solution.

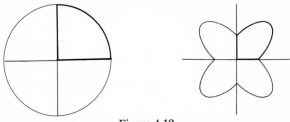

Figure 4.12

PROBLEM 26. The problem is: Find the surface of given area S, one part of which is a fixed circular disc of area A $(2A < S)$, which includes the greatest volume.

PROBLEM 27. *Hint.*

$$\overline{PF_1} = \overline{PP_1} \quad \text{and} \quad \overline{PF_2} = \overline{PP_2}$$

because tangents to the same sphere from a point outside have equal lengths.

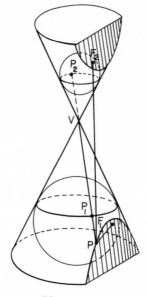

Figure 4.13

PROBLEM 28. Let T be any point on the hyperbola (see Fig. 4.14). Connect it with the foci F_1 and F_2, and draw the bisector l of the angle F_1TF_2. We shall show that l is the tangent by proving that any other point P of l does not lie on the hyperbola. Let F_2' be the reflection of F_2 in l, and connect P with F_2, F_2' and F_1. Now,

$$| \overline{PF_2} - \overline{PF_1} | = | \overline{PF_2'} - \overline{PF_1} | \leq \overline{F_1F_2'}$$

$$= | \overline{TF_2'} - \overline{TF_1} | = | \overline{TF_2} - \overline{TF_1} |,$$

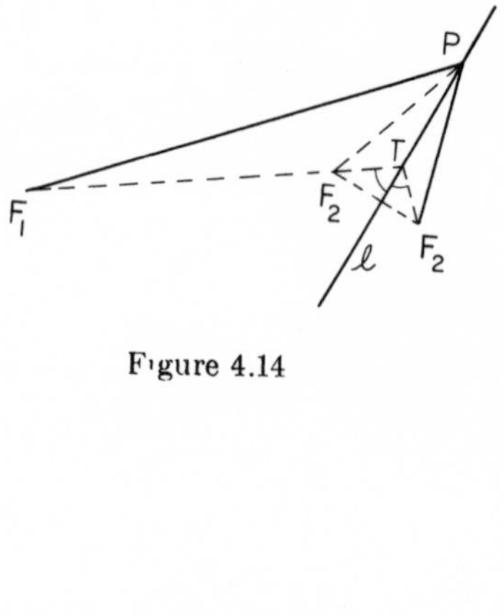

Figure 4.14

and the sign of equality holds only if the points P, F_2', and F_1 are collinear. This is the case only when P is T. Thus l meets the hyperbola in one point only, and all other points lie on that side of the hyperbola for which

$$| \overline{PF_2} - \overline{PF_1} | < | \overline{TF_2} - \overline{TF_1} | = \text{constant} = k.$$

We may call this side the "outside" of the hyperbola. Note that the "interior" of the hyperbola, that is, all points P for which

$$| \overline{PF_2} - \overline{PF_1} | > k,$$

consists of two disjoint regions of the plane.

PROBLEM 29. *Hint.* The bisectors of the vertical angles formed by two straight lines are perpendicular.

PROBLEM 30. The dashed line-segment joining P to P in Fig. 4.15 is the image of a path on the table from P to P. A point of intersection of this line-segment with a side of a rectangle is a point where a ball is reflected from a side of the billiard table, or it is an image of such a point. Such a path, for example, is given by $P \rightarrow w \rightarrow x \rightarrow y \rightarrow z \rightarrow P$. To find a possible path from P to Q, connect P to any one of the images of Q obtained by reflections.

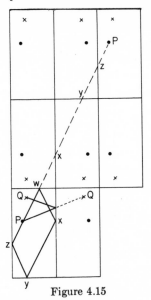

Figure 4.15

Other possible shapes for which infinitely many solutions are easily found are the equilateral triangle and the regular hexagon. Are there any others? What shapes may a polygonal tile have so that you can cover a plane completely, and without overlapping, with identical replicas of this tile?

PROBLEM 31. The n-gon of least perimeter which can be inscribed in a given convex n-gon has the following property: two adjacent sides of the minimal n-gon make equal angles with the side of the given n-gon which contains their common vertex.

PROBLEM 32. Consider Fig. 4.16. The hexagon $AP_1CP_2BP_3$, obtained by reflecting P in each side of the triangle, has area $2T$ and perimeter $2(\overline{PA} + \overline{PB} + \overline{PC})$. From the statement following Problem 21 we have: of all hexagons of area $2T$, the regular hexagon has the least perimeter. Denote this perimeter by L. Then

$$2(\overline{PA} + \overline{PB} + \overline{PC}) \geq L.$$

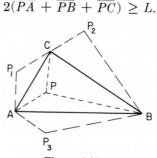

Figure 4.16

By computing the perimeter L of a regular hexagon in terms of its area $2T$, show that

$$L = 4\sqrt{\sqrt{3}\,T}.$$

PROBLEM 33. Of all triangles with a given area T, the equilateral triangle has the largest inscribed circle. Denote its radius by r_E; then

$$r_E \geq r.$$

But the area of an equilateral triangle in terms of the radius of its inscribed circle is

$$T = 3\sqrt{3}\,r_E^2.$$

Therefore

$$\overline{PA} + \overline{PB} + \overline{PC} \geq \sqrt{\sqrt{3}\,T} = 2\sqrt{\sqrt{3}\cdot3\cdot\sqrt{3}\,r_E^2} = 6r_E \geq 6r. \ \blacksquare$$

PROBLEM 34. *Theorem. Let S be a tetrahedron, and construct three triangular prisms which have a common lateral edge and which have for their bases three faces of S, and of which all or none lie entirely outside of S. Then, if one constructs a fourth triangular prism on the remaining face of S whose lateral edges are translates of the common lateral edge of the first three prisms, the sum of the volumes of the first three prisms is equal to the volume of the fourth prism.*

PROBLEM 35. Use the hint and Theorem 3 to obtain the inequality

$$a \, \overline{PA} \cdot b \, \overline{PB} \cdot c \, \overline{PC} \geq (cp_b + bp_c)(ap_c + cp_a)(bp_a + ap_b),$$

and apply Theorem 8 to each factor on the right.

PROBLEM 36. We first consider a special case.

THEOREM. *Let ABCD be a tetrahedron all of whose faces have equal area, and let P be a point in its interior. Then*

$$\overline{PA} + \overline{PB} + \overline{PC} + \overline{PD} \geq 3(p_a + p_b + p_c + p_d),$$

where p_a, p_b, p_c, p_d are the distances from P to the faces. Equality holds if and only if the tetrahedron is regular and P is its center.

PROOF. Let the common area of the faces be S. Using the generalized Pappus Theorem of Problem 34, we can show that

$$(1) \qquad \overline{PA} \cdot S \geq p_b \cdot S + p_c \cdot S + p_d \cdot S$$

in a manner analogous to that in the proof of the Erdös-Mordell Inequality for triangles.

Observe that in proving (1) we did not make use of any properties distinguishing one vertex or face of the tetrahedron from any other vertex or face. Therefore, since we were able to prove the inequality (1) which singled out the vertex A, we must be able also to prove the corresponding inequalities involving the other three vertices. Once we become aware that the left member of inequality (1) involves the distance from P to the vertex A and that the right member involves the distances from P to the three faces which meet at A, and once we understand our notation,† we can write down the other three inequalities:

---

† In our notation, we merely consider the four letters a, b, c, d and perform all cyclic permutations; each time we capitalize the first letter which will distinguish the vertex treated in each inequality. Thus, we consider A, b, c, d; B, c, d, a; C, d, a, b; D, a, b, c.

(2) $\overline{PB} \cdot S \geq p_c \cdot S + p_d \cdot S + p_a \cdot S,$

(3) $\overline{PC} \cdot S \geq p_d \cdot S + p_a \cdot S + p_b \cdot S,$

(4) $\overline{PD} \cdot S \geq p_a \cdot S + p_b \cdot S + p_c \cdot S.$

Adding corresponding members of all four inequalities above, we obtain the desired inequality. ∎

If the tetrahedron is a regular one and if the point P is the center of its circumsphere, then

$$\overline{PA} + \overline{PB} + \overline{PC} + \overline{PD} = 3(p_a + p_b + p_c + p_d).$$

However, what might seem to be the natural generalization of the Erdös-Mordell Inequality, namely, the inequality

$$\overline{PA} + \overline{PB} + \overline{PC} + \overline{PD} \geq 3(p_a + p_b + p_c + p_d),$$

does not hold in general. In particular, it does not hold for the degenerate tetrahedron illustrated in Fig. 4.17. Find a non-degenerate tetrahedron for which it does not hold.

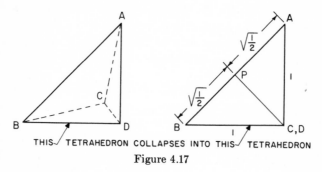

THIS TETRAHEDRON COLLAPSES INTO THIS TETRAHEDRON

Figure 4.17

One might now conjecture that

$$\overline{PA} + \overline{PB} + \overline{PC} + \overline{PD} > 2\sqrt{2}[p_a + p_b + p_c + p_d].$$

This conjecture has been verified for all trirectangular tetrahedra (three faces mutually perpendicular) and for all tetrahedra which contain the centers of their circumscribing spheres. D. K. Kazarinoff had a proof of the general result, but he refused to divulge it, perhaps because it was too complicated. Can you find a proof?

One might also consider inequalities involving distances to edges and vertices and distances to edges and faces. Can you make any conjectures? Can you prove any theorems?

PROBLEM 37. If the quadrilateral is convex, the desired point is the point of intersection of its diagonals. This is an immediate consequence of the fact that the straight-line distance is the shortest distance between two points. If $ABCD$ is not convex and D lies inside ABC, D is the desired point.

PROBLEM 38. *Solution* 1. Let the point P lie inside ABC, and move P so that $\overline{PC}$ is constant (see Fig. 4.18). Then by the reflection principle, $\overline{PA} + \overline{PB}$ is a minimum when $\angle APC = \angle BPC$. In this case the mirrors, which are the tangents to the circle traced by P, vary in position; for each mirror, P is the point of tangency, and there is exactly one point on the circle at which the tangent mirror reflects a ray issuing from A in such a way that the reflected ray reaches B (see Fig. 4.19). "Whatever" property the minimizing point P has with respect to C, it must have the same property with respect to A and B as well. Therefore, we conclude that the angles APC, BPC, and APB must all be equal at that point P the sum of whose distances to the vertices A, B, and C is least. But this is possible only if no angle of the triangle is greater than $2\pi/3$ (or $120°$).

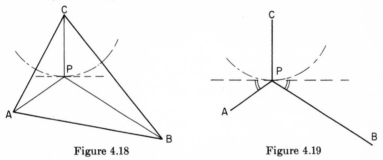

Figure 4.18   Figure 4.19

For example, if $\angle A > 120°$, and if $\angle APB = \angle APC = 120°$, then one of the triangles PAB and PAC must have a sum of angles greater than π (or $180°$), which is impossible. One can show that if one of the angles of the triangle is at least $2\pi/3$, then the vertex corresponding to this angle is the point the sum of whose distances to the vertices of the triangle is least. The minimizing point must lie somewhere on a side of the triangle, since it cannot lie inside; further, one can easily see that it must be at the vertex of the largest angle.

Solution 2. Let three holes, A, B, and C, be made in a horizontal table, and let three one-kilogram weights be hung below the table by strings which pass through the holes and which are tied together in a knot P above the table (see Fig. 4.20). The point of equilibrium of the knot is the desired point. This is because in equilibrium the weights have descended so as to minimize their total potential energy, that is, so that the sum $\overline{AA'} + \overline{BB'} + \overline{CC'}$ is at a maximum. But

$$(\overline{A'A} + \overline{AP}) + (\overline{B'B} + \overline{BP}) + (\overline{C'C} + \overline{CP})$$

is constant. Therefore, $\overline{AP} + \overline{BP} + \overline{CP}$ is least at equilibrium. Now, the force in each of the three strings is equal, and three equal forces can be in equilibrium only if they make equal angles with each other. Hence, at equilibrium the angles between the strings at the knot must be equal.

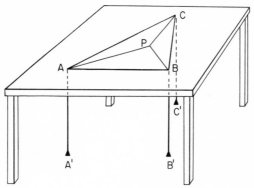

Figure 4.20

Another elegant solution of this problem, together with a simple method of constructing the desired point P, is given in *The Enjoyment of Mathematics*, by H. Rademacher and O. Toeplitz, Princeton University Press (1957), page 34.

PROBLEM 39 (Posed by P. Bartfai, solution by G. Kalman). The possible rhombi at A all have a vertex on the bisector of $\measuredangle A$ (see Fig. 4.21). The largest one of these has a vertex on BC. Thus there are but three rhombi to consider. Let the area of the triangle be T, let the area of the rhombus $ADEF$ be T_a , and let $\overline{AF} = x$. Then

$$T_a = T - [T(CDE) + T(BEF)];$$

and because the ratio of the areas of two similar triangles is the same as the ratio of the squares of the lengths of a pair of corresponding sides, we have

$$T_a = T\left[1 - x^2\left(\frac{1}{b^2} + \frac{1}{c^2}\right)\right].$$

But
$$\frac{b}{c} = \frac{b - x}{x}; \quad \text{hence,} \quad x = \frac{bc}{b + c}.$$

Therefore

$$T_a = T\,\frac{2bc}{(b + c)^2}.$$

Similarly,

$$T_b = T\,\frac{2ac}{(a + c)^2} \quad \text{and} \quad T_c = T\,\frac{2ab}{(a + b)^2}.$$

Now, therefore,

$$T_a - T_b = \frac{2cT}{(a + c)^2(b + c)^2}\,(a - b)\,(ab - c^2),$$

$$T_b - T_c = \frac{2aT}{(b + a)^2(c + a)^2}\,(b - c)\,(bc - a^2),$$

and

$$T_c - T_a = \frac{2bT}{(c + b)^2(a + b)^2}\,(c - a)\,(ca - b^2).$$

If $a \le b \le c$, then $ab \le c^2$; and therefore $T_a \ge T_b$. Also, $bc \ge a^2$; hence, $T_c \ge T_b$. Thus the largest of T_a, T_b, and T_c is either T_a or T_c. T_c is greater than, equal to, or less than T_a according as $ac > b^2$, $ac = b^2$, or $ac < b^2$. ∎

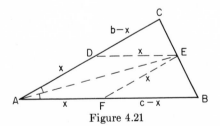

Figure 4.21

The poser of this problem and the author of the above solution were Hungarian high-school students.

PROBLEM 40. By the law of cosines,

$$s_a^2 = \left(\frac{a}{2}\right)^2 + b^2 - ab \cos C, \quad \text{and} \quad s_b^2 = \left(\frac{b}{2}\right)^2 + a^2 - ab \cos C.$$

Therefore

$$s_a^2 - s_b^2 = \tfrac{3}{4}(b^2 - a^2)$$

(see Fig. 4.22). By hypothesis $b > a$. Consequently $s_a^2 > s_b^2$ or $s_a > s_b$. Similarly, $s_b > s_c$.

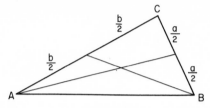

Figure 4.22

We now consider the angle bisectors (see Fig. 4.23). We first extend side BA to a point E such that $\overline{AE} = b$. We then draw the line-segment EC and note that EC is parallel to AD. Since $\triangle EBC$ is similar to $\triangle ABD$,

$$\frac{2b \cos \tfrac{1}{2}A}{b + c} = \frac{f_a}{c}.$$

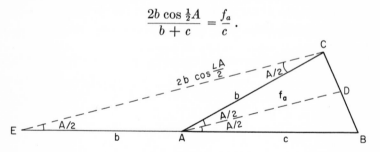

Figure 4.23

Therefore,

$$f_a = \frac{2bc \cos \tfrac{1}{2}A}{b + c}; \quad \text{and similarly,} \quad f_b = \frac{2ca \cos \tfrac{1}{2}B}{c + a}.$$

Thus

$$f_a - f_b = \frac{2c[b(c + a) \cos \tfrac{1}{2}A - a(b + c) \cos \tfrac{1}{2}B]}{(b + c)(c + a)}.$$

Clearly, the sign of $f_a - f_b$ is determined by the sign of the quantity in brackets in the numerator. Since by hypothesis $a < b$, it is true that $\angle A < \angle B$ and that $\cos \frac{1}{2}A > \cos \frac{1}{2}B$. Also, $b(c + a) > a(b + c)$ since $bc > ac$. Therefore $f_a > f_b$. Similarly, $f_b > f_c$. ∎

PROBLEM 41. *Solution* 1. Assume that AB is the longest side; that is, $c > a$, $c > b$. Let PH and CH' be altitudes of the triangles APB and ABC, and consider the similar triangles $PC'H$ and $CC'H'$. Then

$$\frac{\overline{PC'}}{\overline{CC'}} = \frac{\overline{PH}}{\overline{CH'}}.$$

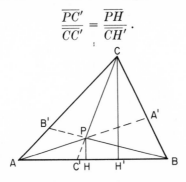

Figure 4.24

Moreover, since triangles PAB and ABC have the same base, the ratio of the lengths of the altitudes PH and CH' is the same as the ratio of their areas. Thus

$$\frac{\overline{PH}}{\overline{CH'}} = \frac{\overline{PC'}}{\overline{CC'}} = \frac{T(PAB)}{T(ABC)}.$$

But $\overline{CC'} < c$ since AB is the longest side of $\triangle ABC$. Therefore,

$$\frac{\overline{PC'}}{c} < \frac{T(PAB)}{T(ABC)}.$$

Similarly,

$$\frac{\overline{PA'}}{c} < \frac{T(PBC)}{T(ABC)} \quad \text{and} \quad \frac{\overline{PB'}}{c} < \frac{T(PCA)}{T(ABC)}.$$

Hence,

$$\overline{PA'} + \overline{PB'} + \overline{PC'} < \frac{c[T(PAB) + T(PBC) + T(PCA)]}{T(ABC)}$$

or

$$\overline{PA'} + \overline{PB'} + \overline{PC'} < \frac{cT(ABC)}{T(ABC)} = c. ∎$$

Solution 2. *Hint.* Draw lines $A''B''$, $B'''C'''$, and $A'''C'''$ through P parallel, respectively, to the sides AB, BC, and AC (see Fig. 4.25). Consider the triangles $PA''C'''$, $PA'''B'''$, and $PC'''B''$. Show that $\overline{PA'} + \overline{PB'} + \overline{PC'}$ is less than the sum of the longest sides of these three triangles and that this sum is the length of the longest side of $\triangle ABC$.

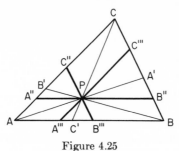

Figure 4.25

Problems 40 and 41 were posed by Hungarian high-school students and by Paul Erdös, also educated in Hungary.

PROBLEM 43. Consider Fig. 4.26. The triangle of least area has H as the midpoint of its base.

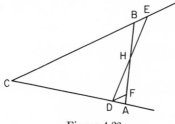

Figure 4.26

PROOF. Call this triangle CDE (see Fig. 4.26). Let ABC be any other allowed triangle, and assume that we have chosen the names of our points in such a way that D lies between A and C. Construct DF parallel to CE, intersecting AB at F. Then the triangles DFH and BEH are congruent. Therefore

$$T(CAB) = T(CDE) + T(DAF)$$

or

$$T(CAB) > T(CDE). \quad \blacksquare$$

PROBLEM 44. *Hint.* The point of tangency must be midway between
AB and CD.

Let EF be the tangent whose point of tangency is midway between
AB and CD. Let $E'F'$ be any other tangent, and let $E'F'$ intersect
EF at X (see Fig. 4.27). Then $T(EXE') < T(FXF')$ if X is closer
to AB than it is to CD. However, one must say a little more, as Fig.
4.28 shows.

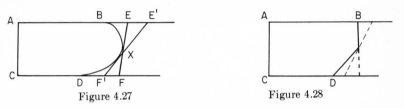

Figure 4.27   Figure 4.28

PROBLEM 45. Suppose the sphere has unit radius. It is trivial
that $S_2 = \pi$ and $S_3 = 2\pi$. To find S_4, let the four points be named
1, 2, 3, and 4, and consider the four possible distinct triples of these
points. Clearly, for each triple the sum S is less than or equal to S_3;
that is,

$$S(1, 2, 3) \leq S_3, \qquad S(2, 3, 4) \leq S_3,$$

$$S(1, 2, 4) \leq S_3, \quad \text{and} \quad S(1, 3, 4) \leq S_3.$$

But

$$S(1, 2, 3) + S(2, 3, 4) + S(1, 2, 4) + S(1, 3, 4) = 2S(1, 2, 3, 4).$$

Therefore

$$2S_4 \leq 4S_3$$

or

$$S_4 \leq 2S_3 = 4\pi.$$

Equality holds if and only if each of the four triples of the four given
points is in an extremal position, that is, if and only if the four points
are symmetric with respect to the center of the sphere. For example,
they might lie in pairs at opposite ends of two diameters.

It might be conjectured that, in general,

$$S_{2k} = \pi k^2 \quad \text{and} \quad S_{2k+1} = \pi k(k + 1),$$

since these are the values of S obtained by distributing $2k$ or $2k + 1$
points as evenly as possible on opposite ends of a diameter of the

sphere or in some other symmetric fashion. Because these values of S are attained for some configurations of the points, we know that

$$S_n \geq \frac{\pi}{4} n^2 \quad \text{or} \quad \frac{S_n}{n^2} \geq \frac{\pi}{4}.$$

If we repeat the reasoning by which we obtained S_4 from S_3 to estimate S_n in terms of S_{n-1}, we find that since there are n distinct groups of n points taken $n - 1$ at a time,

$$(n - 2)S_n \leq nS_{n-1} \quad \text{or} \quad S_n \leq \frac{n}{n - 2} S_{n-1}.$$

For example,

$$S_5 \leq \frac{20}{3} \pi.$$

Therefore

$$S_n \leq \frac{n}{n - 2} \cdot \frac{n - 1}{n - 3} S_{n-2} \leq \frac{n}{n - 2} \cdot \frac{n - 1}{n - 3} \cdot \frac{n - 2}{n - 4} S_{n-3} \leq \cdots$$

$$\leq \frac{n(n - 1)(n - 2) \cdots 5}{(n - 2)(n - 3)(n - 4) \cdots 3} S_4$$

or

$$S_n \leq \frac{n(n - 1)}{3} \cdot \pi.$$

Consequently,

$$\frac{\pi}{4} \leq \frac{S_n}{n^2} \leq \frac{\pi}{3} \left(1 - \frac{1}{n}\right) \quad \text{for} \quad n = 4, 5, 6, \cdots.$$

PROBLEM 46. The shortest chord which bisects the area of a triangle is the base of an isosceles triangle whose vertex is the vertex of the given triangle corresponding to the smallest angle. The longest such chord has this vertex as one endpoint.

We first prove the theorem suggested as a hint.

Let $\triangle$ (triangle ABC) and $\triangle'$ (triangle $A'B'C'$) be the given triangles of equal area and unequal legs, say $a > b$, $a' > b'$. Since, by hypothesis, $\angle ACB = \angle A'C'B'$, we may denote each of these angles simply by C. Suppose that $\triangle$ is the triangle with the smaller difference between the lengths of the sides which meet at the vertex C, namely, that

(1) $a - b < a' - b'.$

Our proof will be complete when we have shown that $c < c'$.

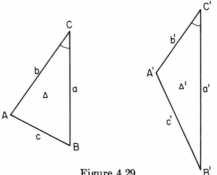

Figure 4.29

Now observe that

$$2T(\triangle) = ab \sin C = 2T(\triangle') = a'b' \sin C,$$

so that

(2) $ab = a'b'.$

From (1) it follows that

$$(a - b)^2 < (a' - b')^2$$

or

$$a^2 - 2ab + b^2 < a'^2 - 2a'b' + b'^2.$$

In view of (2), if we add $2ab$ to each member of the last inequality, it becomes

(3) $a^2 + b^2 < a'^2 + b'^2.$

We wish to prove that

$$c = \overline{AB} < c' = \overline{A'B'}.$$

By the law of cosines,

$$c^2 = a^2 + b^2 - 2ab \cos C \quad \text{and} \quad c'^2 = a'^2 + b'^2 - 2a'b' \cos C.$$

Consequently, in view of (2),

$$c'^2 - c^2 = a'^2 + b'^2 - (a^2 + b^2).$$

It follows from the inequality (3) that the last expression is positive. Therefore

$$c'^2 > c^2; \quad \text{hence,} \quad c' > c,$$

as we set out to prove. ∎

We can now attack the original problem. The theorem we have just proved tells us that the shortest area-bisecting chord is the shortest of the three such transversals which are bases of isosceles triangles, see Fig. 4.30(a). Denote the lengths of their bases by a', b', and c' where the base of length a' lies opposite A, etc. However, it may be that these three triangles do not all exist; for example, for the triangle in Fig. 4.30(b), there is no area-bisecting chord which is the base of an isosceles triangle with vertex at A.

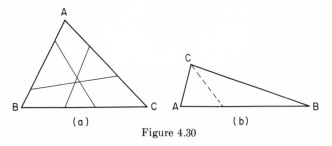

Figure 4.30

It is true that if $\angle C$ is the smallest angle of $\triangle ABC$, then such an isosceles triangle of area $T/2$ having its vertex at C does exist. (We shall call it $\triangle$.) We shall prove the last statement in a moment. First, assuming that the desired isosceles triangle $\triangle$ with base of length c' exists, we note that even if the other such isosceles triangles do not exist, c' must be smaller than the length of any other area-bisecting chord. We show this as follows. The areas of the possible isosceles triangles of area $T/2$ cut off $\triangle ABC$ are

$$\tfrac{1}{4}a'^2 \cot \tfrac{1}{2}A, \qquad \tfrac{1}{4}b'^2 \cot \tfrac{1}{2}B, \quad \text{and} \quad \tfrac{1}{4}c'^2 \cot \tfrac{1}{2}C.$$

If $a \geq b \geq c$, then $\angle A \geq \angle B \geq \angle C$, and

$$\cot \tfrac{1}{2}A \leq \cot \tfrac{1}{2}B \leq \cot \tfrac{1}{2}C.$$

If the three areas above are equal, this means that

$$a' \geq b' \geq c'.$$

Now if, for example, the isosceles triangle of area $T/2$ and with vertex at A does not lie inside of $\triangle ABC$, then by the theorem above, all allowed triangles of area $T/2$ and with one vertex at A have bases longer than a' and hence longer than c'.

It remains to demonstrate that c' exists, namely, that an isosceles triangle with one vertex at the smallest angle C and whose base is an area-bisecting chord does, in fact, always exist. Let x be the length of each leg of the isosceles triangle $\triangle$ with vertex angle C and with area $T/2$. If we could show that $x \leq b$, then we would know that $\triangle$ is the isosceles triangle whose existence we wanted to establish. This is true because the inequality $x \leq a$ would follow from the inequality $b \leq a$ and because the base of $\triangle$ would clearly intersect the sides AC and BC.

To prove that $x \leq b$, note that

$$\tfrac{1}{2}T = \tfrac{1}{4}ab \sin C \qquad \text{and} \qquad \tfrac{1}{2}T = \tfrac{1}{2}x^2 \sin C,$$

so that

$$x^2 = \tfrac{1}{2}ab.$$

By the triangle inequality,

$$a < b + c;$$

and by hypothesis,

$$c \leq b.$$

Therefore

$$a < 2b;$$

hence,

$$x^2 < \tfrac{1}{2} \cdot 2b \cdot b = b^2 \qquad \text{or} \qquad x < b.$$

Our proof is now complete. Of course, in the case of an isosceles triangle with $c = b \leq a$, the "shortest" area-bisecting transversal is not unique, and in an equilateral triangle there are three such transversals.

Next we may ask: Which is the longest area-bisecting chord? The same theorem we used to answer the "shortest transversal question" shows that the longest area-bisecting chord of a triangle must have one endpoint a vertex of the triangle. It follows that this chord is a median of the triangle. Of the three possibilities, one can show by a simple (not necessarily short) computation that the longest is the one terminating in the shortest side. *Hint.* Let ABC be any triangle with $a \geq b \geq c$. Let AA', BB', and CC' be area-bisecting chords. Show that

$$4\,\overline{AA}'^2 = 2c^2 + 2b^2 - a^2$$

and

$$4\,\overline{CC}'^2 = 2b^2 + 2a^2 - c^2;$$

therefore

$$4(\overline{CC}'^2 - \overline{AA}'^2) = 3(a^2 - c^2) \geq 0,$$

from which the inequality

$$\overline{CC}' \geq \overline{AA}'$$

follows. Show similarly that $\overline{CC}' \geq \overline{BB}'$.

PROBLEM 47. The shortest chord is the base of an isosceles triangle whose vertex is the vertex of the smallest angle of the given triangle; the longest chord has one endpoint at this vertex.
Hint. First prove this:

THEOREM. *Of two triangles ABC and $A'B'C'$ with $\sphericalangle ACB = \sphericalangle A'C'B'$ and which have a common sum of the lengths of their legs, that is,*

$$a + b = a' + b',$$

the one with the smaller difference between the lengths of its legs has the shorter base.

PROOF. We use the same notation as in the solution to Problem 46; we wish to prove that

$$c' > c,$$

given that

(1) $$a + b = a' + b',$$

(2) $$a - b < a' - b'.$$

Now the condition (1) is equivalent to the equality

$$a'^2 + b'^2 - (a^2 + b^2) = 2(ab - a'b'),$$

and by the law of cosines, our desired result $c' > c$ is equivalent to the inequality

(3) $2(a'b' - ab) \cos C < a'^2 + b'^2 - (a^2 + b^2).$

It therefore suffices to show that

$$2(a'b' - ab) \cos C < 2(ab - a'b') = -2(a'b' - ab)$$

or, equivalently,

$$(a'b' - ab)[\cos C + 1] < 0.$$

Now, the inequality

$$a'b' - ab < 0$$

can be deduced by squaring right- and left-hand members of (1) and (2) and subtracting, while the inequality $1 + \cos C > 0$ is equivalent to the statement $\angle C \neq \pi$, which is necessary if we are to have a triangle at all. Hence, (3) is indeed valid, and $c' > c$. ∎

INDEX OF NUMBERED THEOREMS

1. If $a > b$ and $b > c$, then $a > c$.   9

2. If $a > b$ and $c \geq d$, then $a + c > b + d$.   10

3. If $a > b > 0$ and $c \geq d > 0$, then
   (1) $ac > bd$ (2) $ac > bc$ and (3) $1/a < 1/b$.   10

4. If $a > b > 0$ and if $p > 0$, then $a^p > b^p$; if $p < 0$, then $a^p < b^p$.   11

5. For every positive integer n
   $$2\sqrt{n+1} - 2\sqrt{n} \;<\; 1/\sqrt{n} \;<\; 2\sqrt{n} - 2\sqrt{n-1}.$$ 14

6. If $a_i > 0$ $(i = 1, \cdots, n)$ and if $a_1 \cdot a_2 \cdot\; \cdots\; \cdot a_n = 1$, then $\sum_1^n a_i \geq n$, with equality holding if and only if $a_i = 1$ for each i.   19

7. If $a_i > 0$ $(i = 1, \cdots, n)$ and if $\sum_1^n a_i = nA$, then $a_1 \cdot a_2 \cdot\; \cdots\; \cdot a_n \leq A^n$ with equality if and only if $a_1 = a_2 = \cdots = a_n$.   20

8. If $a_i > 0$ $(i = 1, \cdots, n)$, then $\sqrt[n]{a_1 \cdot\; \cdots\; \cdot a_n} \leq \sum_1^n a_i/n$ with equality holding if and only if $a_1 = a_2 = \cdots = a_n$.   24

9. The Isoperimetric Theorem
   (A) Of all plane figures with a given perimeter, the circle has the greatest area.   30
   (B) Of all plane figures with a given area, the circle has the least perimeter.   30

   For Three-dimensional Space
   (A) Of all solids with a given surface area, the sphere has the greatest volume.   30

(B) Of all solids with a given volume, the sphere has the least
surface area.   30

10. (A) Of all triangles with a common base and perimeter, the isosceles triangle has the greatest area.   32
(B) Of all triangles with a common base and area, the isosceles
triangle has the smallest perimeter.   32

10A′ If two triangles have the same base and the same perimeter, the
one with the smaller difference in the lengths of its legs has the
larger area.   32

11A. Of all triangles with a given perimeter, the equilateral triangle
has the greatest area.   38

11B. Of all triangles with a given area, the equilateral triangle has the
least perimeter.   42

12. Of all n-gons inscribed in a given circle, the regular n-gon has the
greatest area.   44

13. Of all quadrilaterals with a given area, the square has the least
perimeter.   48

14. A quadrilateral with given sides has the greatest area when it can
be inscribed in a circle.   50

15. Of all quadrilateral prisms with a given volume, the cube has the
least surface area.   51

16. Given any n-gon which does not have all its sides of equal length,
one can construct another n-gon of a larger area, with the same
perimeter and with all sides of equal length.   54

17. Given an acute-angled triangle, the vertices of the inscribed triangle with the smallest perimeter are the feet of the altitudes of
the given triangle.   77

18. (Erdös-Mordell) If P is any point inside or on the boundary of a
triangle ABC, and if p_a, p_b, and p_c are the distances from P to the
sides of the triangle, then $\overline{PA} + \overline{PB} + \overline{PC} \geq 2(p_a + p_b + p_c)$,
with equality if and only if $\triangle ABC$ is equilateral and the point P
is its circumcenter.   78

19. (Pappus) Let ABC be any triangle. Let $AA'C'C$ and $BB''C''C$ be
any two parallelograms constructed on AC and BC respectively,
so that either both parallelograms are outside the triangle or both
are not entirely outside the triangle. Prolong their sides $A'C'$ and
$B''C''$ to meet in P. Construct a third parallelogram $ABP''P'$ on
AB with AP' parallel to CP and $\overline{AP'} = \overline{CP}$. The area of $ABP''P'$
is equal to the sum of the areas of the parallelograms $AA'C'C$ and
$BB''C''C$.   84